F. M. BURNET

VIRUSES AND
MAN

Keith E. Evans.

1960.

PENGUIN BOOKS

Penguin Books Ltd, Harmondsworth, Middlesex
U.S.A.: Penguin Books Inc., 3300 Clipper Mill Road, Baltimore 11, Md
CANADA: Penguin Books (Canada) Ltd, 47, Green Street,
Saint Lambert, Montreal, P.Q.
AUSTRALIA: Penguin Books Pty Ltd, 762, Whitehorse Road,
Mitcham, Victoria
SOUTH AFRICA: Penguin Books (S.A.) Pty Ltd, Gibraltar House,
Regents Road, Sea Point, Cape Town

—

First published 1953
Second edition 1955

Made and printed in Great Britain
by Wyman and Sons Ltd
London, Reading and Fakenham
Collogravure plates by
Harrison and Sons

PELICAN BOOKS

A265

VIRUSES AND MAN

F. M. BURNET

CONTENTS

SOURCES OF PLATES

1. *Journal of Experimental Medicine*, 62: 65, 1935 (R. F. Parker and T. M. Rivers)

2. *Nature*, 161: 464, 1948 (Dawson and Macfarlane)

3. *The Journal of Bacteriology*, 54: 637, 1947 (Rake)

5-6. *The Journal of Biological Chemistry*, 165: 241, 1946 (Hook *et al.*)

8-11. *The Lancet*, 1949, Vol. 1, 602. Electron micrographs made by Chu Dawson and Elford at the National Institute of Medical Research; Prints from Elford

13. Dr F. V. MacCallum Colindale; *Virus and Rickettsial Diseases*, Arnold, London, 1950

15-17. Australian Commonwealth Government Department of Information; photographs taken at the Hill Institute, Melbourne, 1946

18-20. The Director, Commonwealth Serum Laboratories, Melbourne, Australia; photographs by the late Dr Julian Smith

Nos. 4, 7, 12, 14 are reproduced from photographs by the author.

CHAPTER ONE

INTRODUCING VIRUSES

AT the beginning of this century the germ theory of disease was firmly established, and in outline at least the ways by which bacteriological knowledge could be applied to the prevention or cure of infectious disease had been worked out. Effective application has followed, and the social results have been probably as significant for the history of the twentieth century as its wars and political revolutions. But the impact of infectious disease on human populations and the consequences of the removal of disease as an effective controlling factor on excessive increase are not the theme of this book. We are concerned with a phase of the scientific study of disease that rather unexpectedly grew out of the spectacular successes of the early bacteriologists. For a good many years now research on viruses has been an important part of the activities of men who work in bacteriological laboratories, and gradually this work has grown in status till it can now fairly claim the title of a distinct science – virology. The name is not a very happy one, and virologists, particularly British ones, still feel somewhat uncomfortable at being so referred to. This book then is an attempt to expound some of those aspects of the new science of virology that are relevant to matters of normal human interest.

Perhaps it is advisable to say first a little about the beginnings of effective research into the causes of infectious disease and the way in which the study of viruses grew out of the simpler studies of bacteria. The first infectious disease from which the 'cause' was isolated as a bacterium was anthrax of sheep. Anthrax is the result of the invasion of the body by a

particular rod-shaped micro-organism which multiplies freely
in the tissues and the blood. Vast numbers are present in the
blood of an animal dying of anthrax and the organism is readily 'isolated' from such blood by the modern form of Koch's
technique of plating. The blood is diluted and a drop spread
over the surface of a jelly solidified with agar and containing
a variêty of nutrient substances from meat extract and the
like. The surface is allowed to dry and then the plate with its
cover is placed in an incubator at body temperature. In
24 hours each anthrax bacillus has multiplied so much that
its descendants have built up a visible 'colony' which to the
naked eye is a flat whitish excrescence with a whorled medusa-
head texture. Under the microscope the colony can be seen to
be made up of millions of tiny rods often attached end-to-end
in long strings. If the colony is dispersed in a large amount of
sterile fluid, and this again plated, similar descendant colonies
appear, and the process can be continued indefinitely. Provided certain technical requirements are fulfilled the anthrax
bacillus, after a hundred transfers and many thousands of
generations, is still capable of producing fatal anthrax in a
sheep or guinea-pig. That is, its disease-producing quality
persists although it is multiplying not in living tissues but in
a simple semi-synthetic mixture of soluble nutrients. It is this
capacity to multiply and retain virulence on simple non-living
nutrients that is the essence of the 'isolation' of a bacterium
as the cause of an infectious disease.

In the two decades (1880–1900) that followed the development of classical bacteriological methods by Koch there was
a flood of discoveries which established the bacterial causes
of many of the most important human diseases. Once the
techniques of pure culture methods had been grasped any one
of Koch's young men could feel that there was a wide open
field from which he could reap a harvest of discovery – Why
should not all disease be due to bacterial action? Cultures

were made from every sort of disease condition and soon the
bacteria responsible for anthrax, tuberculosis, diphtheria,
typhoid fever, cholera, plague, and dysentery had been isolated. Many other bacteria were isolated which enthusiasts
hoped uncritically were the causes of cancer, epilepsy, malaria
or yellow fever, and dozens of other diseases now known to
have no relation whatever to bacteria. The processes of scientific investigation went on, research, publication, criticism of
alleged discoveries, repetition of experiments with confirmation or refutation. It gradually became clear that by no means
all diseases, not even all frankly infectious diseases, were
caused by bacteria that could be isolated by Koch's methods.

Quite early in the history of bacteriological research Pasteur
and Chamberland in Paris found that it was possible to free
a liquid from bacteria by filtering it through unglazed porcelain. This technique had some obvious applications in bacteriological research and its use led to the first demonstration by
Beijerinck in Holland that a disease could be due to an agent
so much smaller than a bacterium that it would pass readily
through one of these filters. Beijerinck was working with the
mosaic disease of the tobacco plant. If the juice expressed
from the leaves of infected plants was diluted in water and
then passed through a porcelain filter the clear filtrate was
still capable of producing the disease when it was rubbed on
to the leaf of a young tobacco plant. The virus of tobacco
mosaic disease was thus the first filterable virus to be discovered, and throughout the history of virology it has maintained a position at the very centre of interest. In 1935 it was
prepared in the form of a pure protein – an extremely large
protein molecule admittedly, but still something better described as a molecule than as an organism. This book is concerned primarily with the virus diseases of man, and we shall
of necessity have to omit any further reference to what many
of us think is an almost wholly unrelated field – the plant

viruses and the diseases for which they are responsible. It is a subject as fascinating as our own, but techniques and even ideas have diverged so much that virtually nothing that we know of plant viruses is relevant to our problems.

Nevertheless the knowledge of the filterability of the tobacco virus was probably at the back of the minds of two German bacteriologists, Frosch and Dahlem, when in 1900 they found that foot-and-mouth disease of cattle was also due to an agent that would pass through a bacteria-proof filter. For something more than twenty years from this first discovery of a filterable virus responsible for an animal disease there was a period of progressive but rather muddled advance in the field of the human and animal diseases from which no responsible bacteria could be isolated. Bacteriologists tended to regard any disease that could be transmitted experimentally from the natural disease to some laboratory animal, like the guinea-pig or rabbit, as due to a 'filterable virus' if no bacteria could be incriminated as the agent. Unfortunately two of this group, which had been studied experimentally for very many years, the cow-pox of Jenner and the rabies with which Pasteur gained such renown, failed completely to come through the usual porcelain filters! Between the two world wars knowledge developed more rapidly, and it gradually became clear that filterability was a very chancy property depending on a wide variety of circumstances. What really distinguished the infectious diseases which could not be ascribed to the visible and usually cultivable bacteria, protozoa, or fungi, was the inability of the agents to multiply on anything less complex than the interior of a living host cell. The term 'filterable virus' was quietly contracted to 'virus', and what had originally been a rather vague general term for anything – poison or infectious agent, which could produce disease, became the name of a fairly well characterized group of micro-organisms.

There are still people who would say that to call viruses

micro-organisms is to make a premature decision on the most important question presented by the group. Are they living or not living? Those who ask that question are usually thinking of the plant viruses which we have excluded from discussion. I think that those who have studied the animal viruses are all agreed that from the practical point of view viruses behave as if they were living organisms. The public health man and epidemiologist are presented with just the same sorts of problems whether the disease is due to a virus like yellow fever, to a protozoon like malaria, or to a bacterium like bubonic plague. In the laboratory technical methods differ, but in the behaviour of a virus one can recognize the individuality persisting from generation to generation, the occurrence of mutation and the play of environment in determining which mutant shall survive under given conditions – evolution in miniature – and the possibility of death, i.e. permanent inactivation by heating and so forth. These are the essentials of life, and I do not think anything is to be gained by pretending that viruses may not really be alive even if it is convenient to think of them as such.

We can define a virus then as a micro-organism responsible for disease which is capable of growth only within the living cells of a susceptible host – and which is normally considerably smaller than any bacterium.

The first part of the definition – the dependence of the virus for growth on the living cells of a suitable host – is the essence of the matter, and it is this requirement that determines the form taken by modern techniques for the study of viruses. The first step in their experimental investigation is to find a convenient laboratory host in which the virus being considered can multiply and produce either a typical disease or some other clear evidence of its presence.

Almost all modern biological research is quantitative in character. Some activity must be measured in appropriate units and the change in that activity by some experimental manipulation also measured in the same units. In dealing with a virus, the question always arises as to how much virus is present in such and such a preparation. To take a very simple practical example, the vaccine virus used for vaccination against small-pox is prepared by scraping off the pustules produced by in-fection of the skin of a calf or sheep. The material is finely ground, treated with a mild antiseptic, and stored in the cold. When it is to be issued for vaccination it is essential to know how active it is. Will it produce a regular 'take' in the people to be vaccinated and how long after issue can it be kept before use ?

The method of making such measurements – what we call in the laboratory, titrating the virus – depends on the fact that the rabbit's skin is highly susceptible to infection by vaccine virus and responds like the human skin with a distinct pock or pustule wherever infection has been produced. The procedure is to remove the fur from a large area of skin by clipping and the use of a depilatory paste. The vaccine lymph to be tested is diluted in some sterile fluid in a series of tenfold steps, giving eight fluids ranging from 1 : 10 to 1 : 100,000,000 of the concentration of the initial lymph. A measured drop of each fluid is placed on a suitably marked area of skin and the skin beneath uniformly scratched through the drop with a sharp needle. In a few days' time we find, if the vaccine lymph is of full potency, that all dilutions from 10 to 1,000 give fused masses of pocks; at 1 : 10,000 there are scattered individual pocks, and perhaps a few in the next dilution. Such lymph would be issued for use. But if the same material had by some oversight been left out of the refrigerator in a warm room for a week the result would be quite different. We might find only a few pocks on the 1 : 10 area and none on any of the others. Such material would be quite useless for human vaccination.

This will illustrate the general principles of measuring virus activity. What is observed is the highest dilution of the material which will produce a recognizable effect. If that smallest recognizable effect is taken as one unit of activity we can then state how many units of activity there are in any material which has been titrated (measured) in this fashion. As long as there is some easily recognizable effect it does not matter what the character of that effect is. Often all we can observe is death or survival of the animal to which the virus dilutions have been transferred. In such cases the unit is taken as the amount of virus which on the average gives 50 per cent of deaths and 50 per cent of survivals. In order to obtain reasonably accurate experiments a considerable number of susceptible animals must be used in each measurement. This makes it a practical necessity to use, as far as possible, small, easily-reared animals which can be obtained and looked after in large numbers. There are two species which fulfil the dual requirements of susceptibility to a large number of important viruses and ready availability – the white mouse and the half-developed chick embryo in the egg. Wealthy laboratories of virus research may occasionally use chimpanzees (monkeys are essential for some types of work), but in every virus laboratory in the world mice and chick embryos provide much of the data that are the raw material of virology. In the last year or two, however, a third approach to the experimental study of viruses has swept into prominence – tissue culture. Something needs to be said about each of these three approaches.

For a large variety of diseases the mouse is susceptible; not always or even usually susceptible to infection by simple contact with another infected mouse in the way one child gives measles to another. As a general rule, the virus must be administered by some standardized method so that it reaches the tissue in which it multiplies most readily. For diseases that affect the nervous system of man it is usual to inoculate the virus into the brain of anaesthetized mice. When a mouse is showing typical signs of disease it is killed and the brain removed with special precautions against contamination with bacteria. If the brain is ground up finely in suitable fluid and the tissue fragments removed by centrifugation, the clear fluid will, with most viruses of this group, produce infection in further mice in dilutions to 1 in 10 million. The process can be continued indefinitely.

For the influenza viruses the infection of the mouse is produced by dropping virus-containing fluid into the nose of the anaesthetized mouse in such a way that a standard amount is sucked right into the lungs. One or two other viruses acting primarily on the skin may most conveniently be inoculated on the hairless skin of the pad of the hind foot. As always, what is required is that a sharply-defined effect be produced as a result of infection, death of the mouse, a patch of pneumonia in the lung or a swelling of the footpad, anything which will tell us clearly that active virus was or was not present in the material inoculated.

The chick embryo in virology

The second mainstay of the virus laboratory is the half-hatched chicken in its shell. Here the conditions are not quite so easy to understand as when we convey a virus disease in one way or another to the mouse. With insignificant exceptions, there are no natural infectious diseases of the chick embryo. The shell and the underlying fibrous membrane are there, in fact, to prevent the entry of any sort of infection. The contents of an egg are sterile, i.e. free from bacteria, from the time it is laid till the chick cracks the shell with the knob on the tip of its beak.

It is highly unnatural to drill a hole in the shell and inject virus-containing material into the fluids or tissues of the embryo, but this very unnaturalness is in part responsible for the effectiveness of the method. The young, growing, and differentiating cells are so well protected mechanically that there is no need for them to possess subtler means of defence against infection. If any one of many different sorts of virus is implanted so as to reach these cells, the virus units invade and multiply in the cells often more freely than they would in the cells of an animal naturally subject to the disease. What happens in the embryo is often very different from what happens in the human patient, but from the point of view of the research man all that is required is that the virus should do

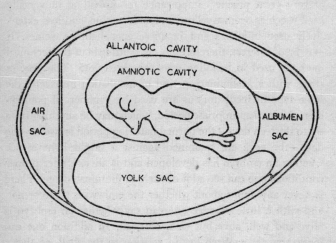

Fig. 1. Diagram of the cavities of a half-developed chick embryo.

two things. It must multiply freely so that if necessary we can 'harvest' large quantities of fresh active virus from an embryo infected with a very small amount. Secondly, the virus in multiplying must produce some change in the embryo that can be used as an index of its presence and amount. Some viruses multiply so extensively that they kill the embryo in a day or two. Others are less lethal, and we may have to observe pock-like spots produced on some membrane or to remove some of the fluid and show that virus is there by some test-tube procedure. Just as with mice, the commonest use of the chick embryo is to measure the amount of virus in a given material by the dilution method I described previously. Again it does not matter what form the virus action takes – as long as it is something we can recognize as undoubtedly due to the virus, it will allow us to do what we want.

During World War II the developing chick embryo became of very great practical importance for providing universally used vaccines against yellow fever and typhus and less extensively used influenza and Japanese encephalitis vaccines. It may be of interest, therefore, to say a little about the technical methods used in handling eggs for virus work. The process starts with a preliminary period of incubation in exactly the same type of incubators as are used by commercial poultry-men. After an appropriate period, which may be anything from six to thirteen days – the normal hatching period is twenty-one days – the eggs are examined against a bright light to see whether an embryo has developed and is alive. Under proper conditions one can see a lot in such an illuminated egg. There is never any doubt about whether the embryo is there or not, and with a little practice one can say whether an embryo is alive and well, alive but sick, or dead. In addition one can mark how the embryo lies in relation to the shell, so that a hole can be drilled at the spot most convenient for the inoculation of the required tissue or cavity.

Unfertile eggs and dead embryos are discarded. Satisfactory eggs are now drilled over the proper area with an abrasive disc mounted on a dental engine. Sometimes no more is required than a hole large enough to allow a hypodermic needle to pass; for some other work a relatively large area of shell is removed to allow what amount to minor surgical operations to be made on the embryo.

The eggs are now ready to be inoculated by whatever method is most appropriate. The first method to be developed made use of the outer living membrane by which the embryo obtains its oxygen from the air, technically the chorioallantoic membrane. The membrane is 'dropped' by making a hole into the air-space at the blunt end of the egg and gently sucking down the respiratory membrane so that it lies at the bottom of a little artificial cavity. This gives us a sheet of cells on which viruses can be grown in much the same fashion as bacteria on one of Koch's plates.

Sometimes one has to inoculate the virus into one of the veins running over the surface of the membrane. This sounds an extremely difficult thing to do, but by the simple trick of putting a drop of liquid paraffin on the opaque white shell membrane, this becomes quite transparent and one can see the vein clearly. To inject virus into the vein then requires merely a syringe with a very sharp needle and a steady hand.

The commonest method is to inoculate the virus into one of the cavities – the allantoic cavity, the yolk sac, or the amniotic cavity. Each has its particular uses, and the first two are used in preparing the virus vaccines which are made commercially. For large-scale production procedures can be simplified so that a conveyor belt can be used to bring the eggs past a series of operators each carrying out one phase of the process in the true modern tradition.

When the inoculation is completed and the hole in the shell sealed, usually with a drop of melted wax, the eggs go back into an incubator while the virus develops. 'Harvesting' the virus means essentially the removal of the particular fluid or tissue from the embryo that experience tells us contains the largest amount of virus. It is always important that this should be done in such a way that no contaminating bacteria should be picked up from the shell or elsewhere. This necessity for asepsis is particularly important in vaccine production, and in nearly all commercial plants the method has been adopted of opening the shell with an oxy-hydrogen blowpipe flame. To most people this would seem an inappropriately powerful tool for a trivial job, but its virtue lies simply in the fact that in addition to cutting the shell the tiny flame leaves a sterile edge even if the surface of the egg is heavily contaminated with bacteria.

In discussing different viruses in later chapters some of the special aspects of growing viruses in chick embryos will be described. Here we may simply mention the chief virtues of the chick embryo for the purposes of the virologist.

(1) A mouse or a guinea-pig is a furry little animal whose skin and fur and intestine are heavily infested with bacteria; it may also be suffering from some unsuspected disease. For one reason or other virus infections may rather easily become complicated by the presence of bacteria in what ought to contain only virus. There are well-established methods of recognizing and dealing with such complications, but they add considerably to the difficulties of experimental work. The chick embryo, on the other hand, is a nice aseptic parcel protected by a smooth shell that can readily be sterilized if necessary. With standard technique it is easy to prevent the entry of unwanted bacteria into the egg, and when the virus develops it is obtained free of any other organisms.

(2) The embryonic cells are highly susceptible to a wider range of viruses than any single species of animal, and in most instances more virus can be harvested than would be obtained from the tissues of an animal. This is specially important in the production of vaccines.

(3) The third great advantage is simply the cheapness of the egg and its universal availability. There is much less skilled labour required in buying and incubating a thousand eggs than in breeding, feeding, and maintaining a similar number of guinea-pigs or mice.

One final virtue of the chick embryo may be expressed in the remark of a visitor from another laboratory on being shown an incubator full of inoculated eggs each carrying on the shell blue-pencil hieroglyphics indicating what virus or other material had been used to inoculate: 'It is a real advantage when your experimental animal can be its own name tag.'

Tissue Culture. There is an even more 'unnatural' method of providing living cells for the growth of viruses than inoculating chick embryos. This is to separate cells completely from the living organism and grow them in test tubes or other containers. It has been known for many years that if a tiny fragment of living tissue, especially rapidly-growing embryonic tissue, is placed in a suitable nutrient fluid and provided with the right environment, cells will grow out from the fragment and spread over any supporting surface. It has also been known since 1925 that some viruses would multiply in such cultures. But until 1950 there always seemed to be more convenient methods of handling viruses than by the tedious methods of tissue culture. In that year, however, Enders in Boston showed that the virus of polio could be grown with surprising ease in tissue cultures of human or monkey cells and, more important, that one could recognize by simple microscopic examination of the cultures that the virus *had* grown.

Since then, research on polio has become almost wholly a matter of tissue culture. In 1954, the two types of cell most commonly used were those growing out from fragments of monkey kidney and a special culture of cells that were derived several years ago from human cancer, the so-called HeLa cells. With experience gained from polio work, other fields are being explored, and at least one important virus, that of measles, has been shown to be susceptible to experimental study by this method.

Tissue culture demands a fairly complex technique, but in principle it is the simplest of all approaches to virology. Choose the right type of cell, grow a flat sheet of these cells on glass, add the virus, and when it has had an opportunity to multiply in the cells, examine them to see whether virus-type damage has been produced. With improvements in techniques and the discovery of the most suitable type of cell for each virus, tissue culture may well become the mainstay of future experimental work in virology.

CHAPTER TWO

THE PHYSICAL NATURE OF VIRUSES

FROM the earliest days of bacteriology there has been a peculiar fascination in the contrast between the smallness of micro-organisms and the severity of the diseases they produce. With the discovery of viruses the contrast became even more striking. Here were agents of disease so much smaller than bacteria that they were beyond the range of the best available microscopes. The situation presented a challenge to the microscopist to produce an instrument that could escape the physical limitations of the ordinary microscope and allow viruses to be 'seen' somehow or other. The physicist could say at once that the only way of doing this was to use some finer form of radiation than light to produce the desired image. Around 1925 a successful microscope using ultra-violet light of shorter wave-length than ordinary light was developed, and pictures of some of the larger viruses were obtained. Once the physicists had reached an understanding of the properties of electrons regarded as packets of electro-magnetic waves it was obvious that theoretically at least elect-ron beams could be used to give enlarged images of the objects far below the minimal size needed for resolution with a light microscope. In 1938 von Borries and Ruzka published in Berlin the first pictures of viruses taken by an electron micro-scope. In the intervening period a large number of viruses have been depicted in the electron micrographs and to most people these pictures are liable to represent the highlights of virus research.

I am something of a heretic in believing that what viruses

do and how they do it is very much more important than what they *are*. In recent years we have found out much about the physical and chemical nature of the more easily handled viruses and with the electron microscope we have obtained some beautiful pictures. In some ways this work on the purification and characterization of plant and animal viruses has been one of the great achievements of this scientific generation. It required the use of the most advanced physical and chemical techniques and great ingenuity in devising ways of concentrating milligrams of virus from kilograms of infected tissues. Dr W. M. Stanley received a Nobel prize for his success in such work with tobacco mosaic virus and influenza virus. This was work in the very best traditions of modern biochemistry – and yet there is more than a suspicion that it has not got us very far.

Medical research is based and must be based on two premises: (1) that its objective is to satisfy the universal human desire for health and the prolongation of life, that its function is to strive constantly for the prevention and cure of disease, and (2) that in doing so it must apply to the problems of health and disease all the logical and technical processes that make up the scientific method. Both are equally important, but the first must come first.

From the human point of view the important things about viruses are their virulence, their restriction to certain cells and tissues of their hosts, how they multiply in and damage the cells they infect, their variations and the way in which they provoke immunity of varying strength in the people who have recovered from an attack. So far nothing that has been discovered about the physical and chemical nature of viruses has thrown significant light on any of these characteristics. There are signs that in time we may build upon and elaborate present knowledge of what viruses are to such a point as will make that knowledge of high practical consequence, but to me this seems a long way off. However exciting it may seem to produce clear electron micrographs of influenza virus or to analyse milligrams of the virus particles into their chemical constituents, these are advances that have no immediate bearing on any of the practical problems of influenza.

There is to me a rather curious similarity between the work which has given us the sizes and shapes of viruses and those other studies which have worked out the distances, sizes, and compositions of the stars. Neither has any bearing on everyday life, both offer tribute to the curiosity and ingenuity of men, and both have enormous and sinister implications for the future. The two absolute weapons for the extermination of our species are (1) the type of bomb which will utilize the atomic reactions which give rise to the supernovae, and (2) the virus which will produce a lethal epidemic amongst the enemy but can be rendered harmless to one's friends by their appropriate immunization. When we understand the structure of viruses as well as we do that of the stars we shall doubtless be hard at work constructing the biological analogue of the hydrogen bomb.

The discovery of the basic fact that viruses were 'filterable' afforded a strong presumption that they were smaller than the bacteria which were held back by the filters used. Provided the particles concerned do not stick firmly to the material of the filter, it is legitimate to look on filters of uniform structure as essentially sieves letting through particles whose diameter is smaller than the diameter of the largest pores present in the filter. This is the principle that was used in the first relatively accurate measurements of the size of different viruses. By careful arrangement of the conditions of preparation it is possible to make 'synthetic' membranes of collodion of graded and nearly uniform pore size. If we set up a series of such membranes whose average pore size is known from physical measurements, we can find quite readily which membrane allows a given virus to pass. We start with a clarified virus suspension and under pressure pass 10 cc. of it through each membrane. A portion of the filtrate is then inoculated into animals or embryos sensitive

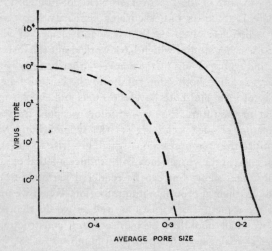

Fig. 2. To show how virus sizes may be determined by filtration through membranes of graded pore size. Continuous line, influenza virus: broken line, vaccinia virus. These lines indicate the amount (titre) of virus found in the fluid which has passed through a filter of average pore size shown on the horizontal scale. Influenza virus passes through filters which hold back vaccinia virus and is therefore smaller.

to the virus in question. Usually each filtrate will be titrated, i.e. tested at a series of dilutions to get a roughly accurate idea of how much virus gets through each membrane. In Figure 2 is shown the sort of result that would be obtained in tests with two well-known viruses that are responsible for epidemic influenza and the virus of vaccine lymph (vaccinia virus) that is used for vaccination against smallpox. It is obvious that vaccinia virus is larger than influenza virus and within a moderately wide range of error the correct size of these viruses was determined well before any electron microscope pictures could be obtained.

It is not quite true to say that viruses cannot be seen with any ordinary microscope. Some viruses can be stained with suitable dyes so that they appear as clearly defined dots under the highest magnification of a good microscope. An important method for the rapid diagnosis of smallpox depends on this fact. But at most no more than a coloured dot can be seen. There is a simple physical reason for this limitation of the microscope. An object can modify the behaviour of a series of waves only if it is not much smaller than the wave-length concerned. If it is very much smaller it will have no more effect than a floating cork has on the waves of the sea. The wave-length of green light is just about twice the diameter of a large virus like vaccinia virus, and this is therefore one of the smallest objects which can be seen.

The electron microscope depends on the fact that a beam of electrons can be made to behave in all essentials like a beam of light of a wave-length about 1/1000 of that of visible light. In place of the glass lenses of a microscope the 'lenses' of an electron microscope are electromagnetic fields of such a type as will bend the stream of electrons in similar fashion, so as to produce eventually an image of the object being looked at, on a photographic plate or fluorescent screen. There are considerable technical difficulties in producing perfectly symmetrical and constant electrical fields, but theoretically there is no reason why the larger protein molecules should not be clearly seen, and the best photographs yet taken show clear detail at a magnification of over 50,000 diameters. On this scale a photograph of a housefly would show it about a third of a mile in length.

In practice it is by no means a simple matter to make effective use of these enormous magnifications. Even with ordinary bacteria one needs to use special staining methods to see them clearly under an ordinary microscope. The everyday routine of examining sputum or pus for tubercle bacilli depends wholly on a method by which the tubercle bacilli are left stained a different colour from all the other bacteria that might be present. Techniques of that sort are not yet applicable to electron microscopy. One cannot, for instance, take a swab from the throat of a patient with possible influenza and put a smear of the material under the electron microscope to check at once whether the influenza is or is not responsible.

There are two main technical difficulties. First, the specimen to be looked at must be set up in a high vacuum and mounted on the thinnest possible film of cellulose. Glass is very opaque to electron beams, and it stands to reason that if we are going to produce a visible effect with something so minute as a virus particle we must mount it on something not very much thicker and of the most uniform possible structure. The second difficulty concerns the material being looked at. Viruses can be obtained in the first instance only in extracts of infected tissues or in the fluids into which virus-damaged cells have been thrown off. Any such material when it is dried down on the cellulose film contains much more non-virus material than virus, and it is usually quite impossible to distinguish the virus particles from the debris of damaged cells. To obtain a satisfactory picture it is always necessary to purify the virus, using those techniques best suited to the problem in hand. For the larger viruses the use of a high-speed centrifuge alone will often produce satisfactory suspensions, but with some viruses all the tricks of modern physical chemistry may be needed to separate the 'gold' from the dross.

Once a pure preparation of virus has been obtained it is placed on a carrier which consists of a tiny disc of fine wire mesh on which lies a very thin film of nitrocellulose. This is inserted into the vacuum chamber of the instrument at the point corresponding to where one places the slide in an ordinary microscope, and then the whole system is brought to a high vacuum. Amongst other things this has the necessary result that everything on the carrier is completely dehydrated – the pictures are essentially of waterless skeletons of what the virus was in nature.

There are several ways of improving the pictures, using means essentially similar to the staining processes employed in bacteriological work. If the virus particles are treated with a chemical containing heavy atoms, osmic acid, for instance, the 'opacity' of the virus to electrons is greatly increased and a sharper contrast with the background obtained. Another ingenious method for enhancing contrast is by what is known as metal shadowing. For this technique the virus preparation on its cellulose carrier is placed in a vacuum chamber and 'bombarded' at a certain angle by free atoms from a hot wire of the appropriate metal, gold or palladium. The atoms adhere to all surfaces that are not shielded by some object from the source of radiation. A spherical object on the membrane thus has the side away from the hot wire source uncoated and also throws a 'shadow' where metal atoms have failed to cover the surface of the supporting film. By suitable photographic methods pictures can be obtained in which the heavily-coated parts appear white and the uncoated shadowed areas dark. These pictures give a striking three-dimensional illusion, virus particles looking like tennis balls scattered over a lawn.

In speaking of the sizes of viruses it is necessary to have some suitable unit, and in microbiology the units of length are the micron, written μ and equal to $1/1000$ of a millimetre, and the millimicron ($m\mu$), which is $1/1000$ of a micron. Perhaps the simplest way to visualize the sort of magnitudes involved is to think of a series of spheres each one-tenth of the diameter of that preceding it. In the first, a centimetre sphere, one could comfortably house a fly, the second, one milli-metre, would take one of the very smallest insects, the third, 100 μ, could be filled by a moderately-sized protozoon like Paramoecium, the fourth, 10 μ, would take two or three red-blood corpuscles, the fifth, 1μ or 1,000 mμ, would be filled by an average bacterium like the staphylococcus that causes boils. We are now approaching the size of viruses, for our next, sixth sphere, is almost the same size as an influenza virus particle, and the seventh, 10 mμ in diameter, is a little smaller than the smallest known viruses, those of poliomye-litis and of foot and mouth disease of cattle.

Some electron micrographs of typical viruses are shown in Plates 1, 2 and 3. Three or four may be taken as covering most of the features seen in such pictures. First we can take the virus of psittacosis, which is a micro-organism easily visible under the ordinary microscope when appropriately stained and with a diameter of about 250 mμ is quite a giant amongst viruses. Electron micrographs show a picture which suggests that the virus is a spherical object surrounded by a rather firm skin, so that when the water is removed in pre-paring the specimen, the surface membrane collapses in folds around the central core of solid matter that is derived by de-hydration of the body of the organism. Many virologists think that the presence of this surface membrane taken along with other characteristics of the psittacosis virus is sufficient for it to be excluded from the 'true' viruses and given a class of its own.

The next of our types is vaccinia virus, which physically and in most other respects is nearly indistinguishable from the virus of smallpox. This is another large virus which when dried on the test membrane takes a rounded rect-angular shape about 200 by 150 mμ. There is no evidence of a surface membrane, but there is an internal structure of some sort which in some ways resembles the nucleus of much larger organisms. When alive and containing the normal amount of water the virus particles are spherical or ovoid, and in this state were clearly photographed by ultra-violet light many years before the electron microscope.

Influenza virus is one which is particularly easy to study under the electron microscope by making use of the capacity of viruses of this group to attach themselves to suitable cells. By suitable treatment the red cells of the fowl can be made to liberate all their content of haemoglobin (the red oxygen-carrying pigment), leaving the thin surface membrane bulged in the centre by the nucleus of the cell. Such cell 'ghosts' dry nicely on the cellulose mounts and give clear photographs. If at the proper stage the cell ghosts are treated with a virus suspension the virus particles attach themselves to the cell surface and show up very clearly in the electron pictures. There are two well-defined forms in which the influenza viruses appear, spheres of about 100 mμ in diameter and long filaments of about the same diameter but up to 100 times that length. The filaments often show some evidence of regularly recurring pattern, but their relation to the spherical forms is not yet clear. More can be said about the circumstances under which the long forms appear when we discuss the reproduction of viruses. Incidentally, the long filament can be seen quite clearly under an ordinary microscope if one uses what is called dark ground illumination. The optical system underneath the specimen is so arranged that no light passes directly into the microscope – only things which, like motes in a sunbeam, are illuminated by light received more or less at right-angles are visible as brightly lit objects against a black background. A suitable preparation from chick embryo fluids will show many bright lines where the filamentous forms of the virus bend and waver in Brownian motion. The spherical forms are also visible, but as featureless spots of light which cannot be distinguished from other fragments in the fluid.

Finally, we may mention the virus of poliomyelitis to exemplify some of the difficulties of electron microscopy. Filtration methods suggest that the virus is very small, around 10–15 mμ in diameter, and it is obvious that in the infected tissues, which are the only source of the virus, the actual amount of virus is very small indeed. If one grinds up normal tissues and carries out the same sort of process as is used in purifying virus it is easy enough to obtain minute granules of tissue particles of the same size as one expects the virus particles to be. This makes it very difficult, in fact almost impossible, to be sure whether the granules from *infected* tissue are virus particles or not. It was only in 1953 that satisfactory pictures of polio virus were obtained, the particles being in the form of tiny uniform spheres, a little larger than the filtration results had suggested.

One thing that should be stressed before we leave these electron pictures of the viruses is that they are representations of the *infective* form of the virus – what is liberated from the damaged cell and is ready to convey infection to the next susceptible cell. It is probable that for some viruses at least the form taken by the virus while it is multiplying inside the cell is very different. One of the main problems of the immediate future is to solve with the electron microscope or otherwise just how this multiplication occurs. The indirect evidence on the matter which we at present possess is discussed in the next chapter.

The chemical structure of those viruses which have been obtained in pure form is more difficult to describe and interpret than their physical forms. Two have been particularly studied, the viruses of vaccinia and influenza. It would be easy enough to transcribe from text-books and papers the elementary composition of each, so much carbon, nitrogen, phosphorus, and so forth. The result would be very much the same as the elementary composition of an average bacterial culture and would tell us nothing beyond the fact that virus particles are not very dissimilar from other living organisms.

Finer analyses have been made, and in broad terms we can say that both these viruses are largely made up of protein, much of it in combination with nucleic acid to form nucleoprotein which is generally regarded as the bearer of hereditary qualities in every type of organism from viruses upward. In addition, both contain fatty substances and complex carbohydrates. One unexpected component of vaccinia virus is a significant amount of copper, which may be a part of some enzyme mechanism, but for which no definite function has been found. By and large, chemical analysis indicates that viruses are simplified organisms made up of the same sort of building stones as other living material.

Perhaps it would not be an altogether unfair summary of our physical and chemical knowledge of viruses to say that it is rather similar to what our knowledge of motor-cars would be if it were limited to a specification of their overall dimensions and of the relative proportions of iron, copper, rubber, water, oil, and petrol in their composition when on the road. Such knowledge would tell us a good deal, but it would leave us very far from being able to make a car or to understand the problems of traffic control in a modern city.

CHAPTER THREE

THE VIRUS AND THE CELL

WE have defined viruses as very small micro-organisms which can multiply only *within the living cells* of a susceptible host. This definition opens up a number of problems which at the present time are matters of the greatest interest to biologists interested in the finer aspects of living process. How does a virus enter the cell it parasitizes, what are the processes by which it multiplies, that is, converts some of the cell substance into virus substance, in what way does it damage the cell, and how is the brood of descendant virus particles liberated so that other cells can be infected?

During the last few years there has been much work going on in the laboratories in an attempt to provide answers to these questions. For technical reasons the work has been concentrated on two types of virus, bacteriophages, the viruses that invade and break up bacteria, and the influenza viruses. Progress has been greater with the bacterial viruses, and what has been discovered in regard to their behaviour has been of the greatest value in pointing towards the most fruitful way of testing influenza virus. It would occupy too much space to give a comprehensive account of the bacterial viruses, but it is worth while to offer a brief description of the process by which one of these viruses enters, multiplies within, and disintegrates its host. Then on the basis of this we can come nearer home and discuss more comprehensively what happens with an influenza virus.

For our bacterial virus we take the commonest of them all with the laboratory name T2 and watch how it attacks an equally common bacterium, the 'B. coli' present in the intestine of everyone. The virus is much smaller than its host and requires the electron microscope to visualize it as a tadpole-shaped object with a spherical body and a short cylindrical 'tail'. The body seems to be filled with the key substance of the chromosomes of typical cells, nucleic acid, while the tail and the sheath around the body are predominantly of protein and are not directly concerned in the process of multiplication.

The first step in the invasion of the bacterium is for the virus to unite with some component of the bacterial wall. The two surfaces stick firmly by virtue of some type of chemical affinity and at their point of union set going a process not yet understood which allows the entry of the important part of the virus, its nucleic acid, into the substance of the bacterium. It seems not unlikely that the two membranes mutually dissolve each other and through the hole the contents of the virus body pass into the bacterium. Here it is necessarily in a form quite different from the original particle. Essentially the virus has been reduced to a collection of hereditary units basically similar to the genes of higher organisms. Most virologists believe that these genes are arranged in strings which can break and rearrange themselves in complex fashions. Each gene in some way abstracts from the host cell the material and the energy required to allow more and more copies of itself to be formed. A 'pool' of genes is built up which eventually almost replaces the proper substance of the bacterium. Then a new process begins. Out of the pool genes come together to form groups in which the right number and the right sorts needed to reconstruct a virus particle are associated. As each group is formed it finds available the proteins needed for the reconstruction of its tail and sheath. Soon there are within the shell of the bacterium anything from 100 to 1000 new virus particles. Then at some time determined by a variety of

factors, the shell of the host disintegrates and the brood of
newly-formed virus particles is liberated.

That description is based on years of careful work by a
large number of scientists and in recent years this has included
the most refined methods of biological and chemical work.
The electron microscope and the use of artificial radioactive
elements have played particularly important parts. I think
that those who are actively working on the problem would
say that my description is a little more straightforward than
is justified by the experimental evidence, but to make the
necessary qualifications would mean going into intolerable
technicalities. What should be stressed is that it is still quite
impossible to describe the process in anything but biological
terms. It is not so long ago that viruses, and especially the
bacterial viruses, were thought to be relatively simple struc-
tures, 'living molecules' which should be amenable to a
straightforward chemical attack. Actually the best description
we can give is curiously similar to and at a lower level of size
hardly less complicated than the invasion of the red blood
corpuscle by the parasite of malaria. There is going to be no
short cut to the secrets of living matter.

Perhaps this conclusion may seem disappointing to the
physicists and chemists who have applied their methods so
effectively to this problem, but it nevertheless represents an
extraordinarily important advance in biology to know that
there are essentially independent living units far smaller than
viruses.

Let us turn now to the influenza viruses to see how very
similar conclusions have been reached about their attack on
the cell. In a later chapter there is an account of how the virus
can be isolated from the throat of a patient with influenza and
much about the disease it produces in mice and men and
chick embryos. Here we are concerned only with the virus as
we handle it in the laboratory by the most convenient available

method. Any of the standard types of influenza virus can be
stored for long periods, either by freezing in a compartment
packed with dry ice (solid CO_2 at a temperature of $-76°$ C)
or by careful drying *in vacuo*. To revive it, a little of the stored
material is injected into the most superficial of the cavities of
the developing chick embryo, the allantoic sac. This is lined
with a uniform sheet of cells highly susceptible to infection
by influenza virus and filled with 5 to 10 cubic centimetres of
what is mainly a dilute solution of the physiological salts.
After two days' incubation at 95° F the cells have been infected, most of them have broken down and liberated the new
virus into the allantoic fluid. It is a very simple manoeuvre to
drain this fluid into a sterile test tube and so give us our
'stock virus'. From one egg we obtain say 8 cc. of slightly
opalescent fluid containing very large numbers of virus particles, around 10^{10}, i.e. ten thousand millions. The actual
weight of virus is not so impressive, being no more than about
1/100 of a milligram; one might call the fluid a 0.0001 per
cent solution of influenza virus.

The amount of virus present can be measured either by
inoculating successive tenfold dilutions of the fluid into other
chick embryos and finding the smallest concentration of virus
that will provoke infection, or by the much simpler process
called haemagglutination.

There are many laboratory tests which make use of the red
cells of the blood, and any bacteriological laboratory can provide a 1 per cent suspension of human red cells washed in
a centrifuge to get rid of the fluid part of the blood and
suspended in a salt solution of proper strength. We take two
tubes each containing one cc. of red cell suspension and add
to one of them (*A*) a drop of allantoic fluid from an egg infected with influenza virus and to the other (*B*) a drop of
allantoic fluid from a similar but uninoculated embryo. The
tubes are shaken and left to stand for an hour so that the cells

can sediment slowly to the bottom. In the tube B with normal
fluid the cells form a little deep red button at the bottom of
the tube, but in A the whole hemispherical base of the tube
is covered with a granular 'shield' of cells sticking to the
glass. If we watch this action of virus-containing fluid on red
cells we find that it consists essentially of a clumping of the
cells into little irregular masses, a process called agglutination, or where red cells are concerned, haemagglutination.

It can be shown that virus particles rapidly attach themselves to the surface of red cells, and if two cells each carrying
a few virus particles collide they will stick together. Some of
the viruses will be attached to both cells and act as bridges
holding them together. It is easy to see that this capacity of
a virus suspension to produce an easily visible effect on red
cells can be utilized as a means of titrating (measuring the
activity of) virus preparations. And by suitable tricks it can be
used for all sorts of secondary measurements – how effectively
a certain chemical or serum will render the virus inactive, for
example. In fact, nearly all experiments with influenza virus
end up with the observation of a series of tubes in some of
which cells are agglutinated, in others not. If physics is based
in the final analysis on pointer readings, our branch of virology is based on the patterns of red cells on the bottoms of
test-tubes.

Haemagglutination by influenza virus is important for two
reasons. First because, as we have just seen, it provides the
basic experimental approach which makes it possible not only
to measure the amount of a virus, but also in ways that need
not be specified in detail to characterize different viruses. One
influenza virus may have been isolated in England in 1933,
another comes from an epidemic on a Pacific island in 1948.
Grown in chick embryos both provide fluids that look alike
and by any normal sort of chemical examination are alike. But
by various experimental manipulations they can be shown to

differ in each of half a dozen respects. Perhaps the simplest is to compare the blood serum of two ferrets, one infected with the 1933 virus, the other with the 1948 one. Mixed with its 'own' virus each serum will prevent that from agglutinating red cells, but it will have almost no action on the opposite one. The viruses are said to differ serologically, a very important difference because it means that after a man has had an attack of one sort he will be immune against that type of influenza for a year or two, but he will not be immune against the other.

The second importance of haemagglutination is intrinsic to the phenomenon itself. This capacity of influenza viruses to stick to the surface of red cells is a manifestation of the same power that allows them to attach to the cells of the air passages and initiate an attack of influenza. By studying the details of the action of virus on red cell it has been possible to show rather clearly how the virus enters the cell that it infects – the first of our fundamental problems of the action of virus on host cell.

Living cells are not simple; even their surfaces are unbelievably complicated chemical mosaics in which complex forms of the three basic components of living tissues are intermingled – protein, fat, and carbohydrate. The fatty material is not ordinary fat, but complex phospholipoids and sterols; the carbohydrate is in equally complex form, large molecules built up of sugars, sugars to which nitrogenous groups are attached, and amino-acids. The common materials most nearly resembling these cell surface components are the grease from wool from which lanoline is prepared and, in the case of the carbohydrate, the sticky materials that we call mucins, phlegm or nasal mucus, the slime on an eel or the track of a snail.

It is the carbohydrate that is important to the influenza virus. Over the surface of either a red cell of the blood or of a cell in the smaller air passages of the lung there is a mesh-work of long molecules of these complex carbohydrates. At many points on this mesh there are chemical groupings which correspond in some sort of lock and key fashion with active spots on the surface of the virus particles. These active spots are built-in enzyme molecules which can both combine with the groupings on the cell surface and when conditions are right destroy them.

This has one very interesting consequence. I have said that if we mix virus and red cells the red cells stick together and clump to the bottom of the tube. But if we use a lot of virus and allow it to act on the cells for a long time, we find that the cells become free again, the virus floats round among them and neither attaches itself to them nor agglutinates them. The carbohydrate groupings of the *receptors* of the cell surface have been destroyed by the virus enzyme that in the earlier stages they had been attached to. In the course of research on the virus enzyme it was found that there were several types of bacteria which produced enzymes with the same general action. The one most closely resembling the virus enzyme comes from the microbe responsible for Asiatic cholera – the cholera vibrio. This cholera enzyme is a straight-forward enzyme, a soluble ferment like the pepsin and tryp-sin of our digestive juices, and it can be concentrated and purified by normal chemical methods. We called this enzyme ' receptor-destroying enzyme' but it is usually referred to by its initials RDE. It is an extremely interesting substance from many points of view. If it is true that to enter a cell the virus must become attached to the carbohydrate receptors, then it should be possible to protect an animal against influenza by temporarily destroying those receptors. RDE is capable of doing just this. In two beautiful series of experiments, Dr Joyce Stone showed that the enzyme could be used to treat mice and chick embryos in such a way that, without damage to the hosts, their cells were rendered insusceptible to virus action and no signs of disease followed the inoculation of the virus. Unfortunately, the experiments have little or no practical significance. The surface of a cell is constantly being remade and when receptors are removed by RDE they have usually regenerated in forty-eight hours and the animal is again susceptible to infection. It is still not clear what is the function of the enzyme on the virus that eventually destroys its attachment to the cell. Perhaps it is a means of liberating the virus after it has entered the cell from the now unnecessary attachment to receptor. There is another suggestion, that it will make it impossible for the virus to be mopped up and rendered harmless by the film of mucus that lines the respiratory passages.

That then is a summary of what we know about how influenza virus enters the cell. The obvious question arises as to whether this is what happens with other viruses too. At the moment it is not easy to answer that question. In addition to the different sorts of influenza virus there is one other human virus, mumps, and one virus capable of infecting man (Newcastle disease of fowls), which show almost the same behaviour. Several viruses which resemble that of poliomyelitis but not the polio virus itself have a rather similar action on some sorts of red cell, and probably future work will show that they, too, have a special means of entering their host cells. For a large group of viruses, however, it is probable that entry into the cell provides no special problems. These are viruses which can infect many different types of cell, including those which are normally prone to take in – to eat as it were – any small foreign particles that get into the body.

It is a more difficult task to determine what happens once an influenza virus – or any other virus – is within the susceptible cell. Only indirect approaches are possible, but sometimes these give us very important information. There are

three important types of experiment that have been made
with influenza virus. The first is to show that one can inject
a mixture of two distinct types of virus into a situation where
single cells may be infected with both and recover virus which
has some of the qualities of both. This production of 'hybrid'
viruses – more correctly recombinant virus – has been clearly
demonstrated for the bacterial viruses and, subject to the
necessity for confirmation by other workers, with equal clarity
for influenza viruses. The second type of experiment is to
inject a virus into a tissue that it does not readily infect and
to show that it enters the cells and damages them. What is
liberated from these infected cells, however, is not virus but
recognizable fragments of virus which can produce effects in
test-tubes but which cannot produce further infection. The
third gives a rather paradoxical finding. A virus which produces the minor damage we have just mentioned can be mixed
with another which is fully virulent for the same tissue and
given alone would provoke a fatal infection. Injected together
in the correct proportions the first 'interferes' with the action
of the second and the animal survives.

The study of what can be called the genetics of influenza
virus has been the chief interest of my own laboratory for the
past five years and, although many new facts have been recorded, it is still impossible to give a satisfactory picture of
what takes place within the cell when the virus multiplies. It
is even harder to express in non-technical language the significance of the experiments which have given relevant information. Perhaps one of the main difficulties is that in virus multiplication we are dealing with a process that has important
analogies to those of genetics but is equally clearly a bio-
chemical process. Now, the languages of genetics and biochemistry are totally different; a gene is the hypothetical unit
of inheritance and in genetic discussion there is no need to
discuss more than its relation to other genes in determining

the nature and distribution of inheritable qualities. At the physical level, a gene is probably a *pattern* carried mutually by a nucleic acid molecule and a protein molecule, but the nature of the pattern cannot be defined in chemical terms.

There are some experimental findings which we can most comfortably discuss in terms of genes, there are others which seem to be concerned with the mutual relationship of protein and nucleic acid and must be discussed biochemically. At a less elegant level the dilemma is probably nearly equivalent to the classic dualism of physics between interpretations based on classical wave theory and those using the particles and discontinuities of quantum theory.

It is probably safe to assume that the first process after a virus enters the cell is for the spherical particle to unfold or dissolve so that its essential units, whether we call them genes or not, can make intimate contact with the nutrition mechanisms of the host cell. In some way these must be persuaded to supply the food-molecules and the energy needed to allow the reproduction of the virus units. This capacity to deviate the activities of the cell from their proper purpose is the essential character of the virus. Where the cell is highly susceptible or the virus highly virulent, the distortion of the cell's activities by this process becomes intolerable and the cell breaks down completely. Even though the cell may appear fairly normal, large amounts of virus material accumulate in its interior – one might almost picture it as a pool of bits and pieces of virus. Once this pool reaches a certain size or concentration, new virus particles begin to form themselves and leak out of the cell. In the case of influenza virus growing in chick embryo cells, this continuous liberation of virus may go on for many hours before the cell becomes grossly damaged.

If two different viruses enter a cell simultaneously each will contribute multiplying components to the pool of bits and pieces, and if the viruses are sufficiently nearly related many of the new brood of viruses will carry qualities derived, some from one, some from the other 'parent'. These experiments will be subject to the same sort of qualifications that would apply to an attempt to assemble automobiles from a complete but unclassified set of components from two different models. Unless the two models were closely similar no hybrid would work. There is much to indicate that most of the hybrid viruses produced are faulty arrangements which will not give rise to descendants, but there are some hybrids which will breed true indefinitely.

When two viruses of the same type enter a cell simultaneously there is also a tendency for badly-put-together virus to be produced as well as normal virus. Such infections give rise to virus which has little power to infect eggs or mice but by the rougher test of power to agglutinate red cells appears to be of normal strength.

If one heats an influenza virus just sufficiently to kill it and no more, this heated virus can still agglutinate red cells and enter a host cell. In many ways it resembles the 'incomplete' virus produced in the course of infection induced by more than one virus particle per cell. Both these types of virus when they enter the cell can render it insusceptible to infection by normal virus reaching it some hours later. This 'interference' by inactive virus with the multiplication of active virus is a widespread happening which may be important for the understanding of some aspects of human disease. In all probability it results from the blocking of a few key components in the susceptible cell. These are hypothetical substances which have never been defined in chemical terms but which must be present in some form or other. When a virus takes on its active multiplying phase within the cell its essential elements attach themselves to these components and thereby set going the process that leads to virus multiplication. The corresponding units from inactive virus lack something needed to set the wheels in motion. They make contact but nothing happens, and by their union with the key components they deny these to any active virus that subsequently enters the cell.

At a more practical level we may mention one or two examples of the way in which qualities from two different influenza viruses can be combined in their offspring. The first example that was described concerned a variant influenza virus with the unusual quality of being able to kill mice by infecting the nerve cells of the brain – what we call in the laboratory a 'neuro'-virus. If any normal influenza virus is inoculated into the brain it will only infect a few cells before it disappears and the mouse will show no symptoms. When the neuro-virus and the ordinary type are inoculated together what happens will depend on the relative amounts used. If the normal virus is in excess it blocks the multiplication of the neuro-virus and the mouse survives. When the amount is just insufficient to prevent symptoms a hybrid form, a recombinant, can usually be isolated from the mixture of viruses in the brain. This has most of the qualities of the normal parent but, in some way or another, it has also taken on the unique brain-invasive quality of the neuro form.

Another type of interaction that has been studied both in Australia and in America results in virus which has, as it were, the surface patterns of both the parents. This can be shown by using two virus types which are neutralized by quite different antibodies. From these one may often obtain virus which is neutralized by *both* antibodies. As a rule, however, this type of double virus does not breed true.

A third type of interaction is a redistribution of virulence when a virulent and a non-virulent type of virus are used to produce double infections. In many instances the progeny can be found to show a wide range of intermediate virulence, in other examples this redistribution does not occur. The reason for these differences is not clear nor is the basis of the redistribution of virulence. Nevertheless, virulence is the most important aspect of any virus and any approach that promises an understanding of virulence must be explored.

This attempt to make a rather complex subject intelligible is justified only by my feeling that it is a subject that is important both for the understanding of general biology and because of its possible consequences at the practical level. If viruses can switch some of their qualities to one another in the laboratory, it behoves us to watch carefully whether some of the changes in character of natural diseases may not be related to the same ability. In the chapter on influenza a hint is given of how such a switch might have had something to do with the appearance of 1918 influenza.

I have spent most of this chapter dealing especially with the behaviour of influenza virus on and in the cell, mainly, I am afraid, because this has been the all-absorbing topic of my own research activities for the last ten years. I do not expect that other virologists think it as important as I do, but unfortunately it is the only virus of man or animals which has yet been studied along these lines. Others may behave similarly or in some different fashion – to find out for any given virus is not easy. In each instance some rather tricky experimental situations have to be contrived before it is possible to undertake anything approaching a detailed analysis of the situation.

CHAPTER FOUR

THE NATURAL HISTORY OF
VIRUS DISEASES

IN the writings of Hippocrates amongst other descriptions of disease there is a clearly recognizable account of mumps, of its symptoms and course, its infectiousness and its tendency to involve older rather than younger children. That is the first clear description of a virus disease. At least, from the time of Hippocrates the object of the physician has been to understand, in order that he can control them, the manifestations of disease. That is still the main objective of the virologist to-day, although he is temperamentally inclined as a rule to stress that he is primarily concerned with understanding and is sceptical of any premature practical applications of his knowledge. Nevertheless the physician and the public health officer must keep on demanding that every advance, whether from the epidemic in the field, from the hospital ward or the laboratory bench, must be incorporated as it arises into the body of medical teaching and practice. So far we have been concerned with viruses and their behaviour from the laboratory aspect almost exclusively. It is time to see how these academic concepts may help to throw light on what happens at the human level. How do viruses produce their symptoms in the body and how are they transferred from one person to another?

In subsequent chapters on some of the common virus diseases the special features of the disease in question will need to be considered. Here we are concerned to see how far a general picture of the process of virus infection can be developed.

In every chapter of this book a single principle is being exemplified in one form or another – that viruses multiply only within living susceptible cells of the appropriate host. The whole natural history of virus infection must be based on this necessity of the virus to enter and multiply within the cell. In the broadest terms the symptoms that are produced depend on the particular groups of cells *which are susceptible to attack and which can be reached by the virus*. The virus of the common cold is limited to the cells living in the upper part of the respiratory system, the virus of poliomyelitis multiplies most readily in those cells of the nervous system that control muscular action. The symptoms of the two diseases obviously depend on these predilections for special cells.

In any infectious disease, whether produced by virus, bacterium, or protozoon, the most important thing that we need to know is how the microbe species survives in nature. We tend to think of infectious disease as simply something which one 'catches' from someone else with the disease. Measles and chicken-pox for most of us provide the pattern – a very simple pattern in which it is very nearly correct to say that the disease is always contracted from another person showing typical symptoms and that the virus survives only by successive transfer from one non-immune human being to another. This, however, is not even the commonest mode by which a disease-producing organism persists from generation to generation. Quite often disease is produced by bacteria which for the most part live perfectly innocent lives either in soil or as harmless scavengers on the surfaces or in the cavities of the body. Their harmful activity results from some special circumstance, such as their entry into the tissues through a wound. Then there are many human diseases due to micro-organisms whose *natural* host is some animal other than man. The most famous of all the great epidemics, the Black Death of the Middle Ages, was due to the plague bacillus which has survived through centuries as a parasite of the burrowing rodents of Central Asia and reached man by way of the black rat.

Within the group of viruses we can recognize two broad patterns of survival. Some viruses can multiply as far as we are aware only within human cells; others can be persuaded in the laboratory to infect cells of other animals, but as far as the natural situation is concerned are not found apart from man. To understand the spread and character of the diseases produced by such viruses we need concern ourselves only with the human situation. The second important group are those viruses whose more usual host is some other animal and which are conveyed to man in accidental fashion, most often by the bite of some blood-sucking insect, mite, or tick. In the spread of virus diseases we do not have to consider the possibility that the organisms can multiply in non-living material. There is no analogy in virus disease to the typhoid epidemic from infected milk, the staphylococcal food poisoning from contaminated cream fillings, or the botulism outbreak from canned vegetables. A virus must pass, usually fairly directly, from infected living cell to a new susceptible living cell.

To understand the natural history of a virus disease we have to consider

(1) how the virus finds it possible to *initiate* infection in one or more cells of the new human or animal host;

(2) how descendant virus passes to other cells of the body and especially to those cells whose destruction or damage gives rise to the symptoms of the disease;

(3) how virus is liberated from the cells so that it can infect a new host;

(4) the process by which the virus passes from one individual of its natural host species, whether man or animal, to another.

The initiation of infection and its spread within the body

It is characteristic of many common virus infections that they have a long incubation period. A girl infected at school brings measles home to a family which includes two younger children. These two will almost certainly show first symptoms twelve days after their sister's rash made its appearance and will be typical spotty cases of measles two days later. It is obvious that the measles virus initiates infection within a few hours of its transfer from the sick child to the susceptible one and that some relatively prolonged process is required before the descendant virus particles burst into activity and are liberated in the throat and on the skin of the patient.

What actually happens in human measles has never been worked out experimentally, because of the extreme difficulty of laboratory work with the virus, plus the intrinsic difficulties of studying human disease before any symptoms are evident. All our deductions as to what takes place in any human virus disease must in fact be drawn from what has been observed in animals experimentally infected with viruses which produce in those animals diseases analogous to the human ones. The resemblance will never be exact, but neither is it likely to be wholly misleading.

There is a natural virus disease of mice which has rather often appeared in laboratory stocks of white mice with results disastrous to whatever experiments were under way. It is a disease closely related to human smallpox, and is best referred to as mouse-pox, though in most technical writings it is called infectious ectromelia. It varies in intensity from one epidemic to another. In some there is a very high mortality, with mice dying within a week of infection, in others the mortality is lower and many mice show seven to ten days after infection a severe skin rash that is essentially similar to the characteristic rash of human smallpox. In yet other outbreaks a very small proportion of mice die and the nature of the disease can be recognized only by special tests.

The whole natural history of mouse-pox has recently been studied by Dr Frank Fenner, now professor of microbiology at the Australian National University. Out of a very extensive investigation reported in more than a dozen papers Fenner has brought together the first clear picture of how the virus of a natural disease spreads through the body and produces its symptoms. Mouse-pox in itself is of no importance except to those who work with mice in laboratories, but it seems reasonably certain that the processes that are concerned in determining the picture of the disease in mice are basically the same as function in all the 'long incubation period' virus infections of man – smallpox, measles, chicken-pox, mumps and so on. This must be the excuse for going into the story of mouse-pox in some detail.

I have called mouse-pox a natural disease of mice, but this is true only in the sense that it occurs unwanted in stocks of laboratory mice. It has never been recognized in mice living under natural conditions, and the ultimate origin of the virus is unknown. As we see it in the laboratories the disease passes readily from infected to uninfected mice introduced into the same cages. Transfer seems to be not by direct contact of mouse with mouse, but by contamination of the environment and infection of minor areas of skin damage. A susceptible mouse will sooner or later suffer a scratch or abrasion, usually around the snout or eyes, and this will be infected from virus present on the contaminated bedding. After a few days the infected region will show itself as a small sore from which the hair has been lost, and in another two or three days the mouse will have a generalized rash over the whole of its skin. In practice of course there will be many variations in the site of the primary sore and in the intensity of the general rash, but the picture is uniform enough to allow an analysis of what occurs between infection and the final healing of the secondary rash. We may summarize Fenner's analysis by saying that he sees a sequence of events:

(1) Infection of skin cells with liberation of new virus that progressively infects local cells of the skin as well as spilling over to some extent into the lymph vessels and blood.

(2) Removal of virus from blood and lymph by scavenging cells in spleen, liver, and lymph nodes.

(3) Infection of highly susceptible cells in liver and spleen with accumulation of virus much of which enters the blood. The damage to the liver may be enough to kill the mouse, but if it survives a fourth phase follows.

(4) Widespread infection of skin (and other) cells to which the virus has been brought by the blood. From each point of infection a local 'pock' may arise by spread through and damage to adjacent skin cells – when a sufficient number of pocks are present we have the secondary rash.

(5) About the time the rash is developing, antibody production is also coming into action. This results in a cessation of further spread of the infection and initiates the healing process.

The picture is probably even more complex than this, but it would be inappropriate to discuss details here. What does emerge clearly is the existence of a local initiating infection, then a complex time-needing process by which the virus builds up its potential, and finally a widespread liberation of virus into the blood with rapid appearance of general symptoms. In these general terms we can give a reasonable account of any of the diseases of long incubation period.

There are, however, virus diseases of *short* incubation period. Influenza for instance can manifest its symptoms within forty-eight hours of contact with a previous victim and may be used as an example of the second important type of spread within the susceptible host. Influenza is not natural to any animal, but it might well become a natural disease of ferrets if ferrets ever collected in numbers like human beings. The symptoms of artificial infection with the virus are similar, and one ferret will pass the disease on to another placed in the same cage. Mice, too, can be infected in a rather different fashion, and from the experimental study of influenza in the two animal species, plus what we can learn from human influenza, it is possible to follow the process of infection.

The influenza virus particle which initiates infection becomes attached by the special mechanism described in Chapter Three to the free surface of one of the cells which line the respiratory passages. In man the important cells are probably those lining the smallest air passages, the bronchioles; in the ferret the cells inside the nasal cavity are particularly susceptible. The virus multiplies and is liberated from the partially destroyed cell, most of it on to the surface of the lining membrane. Only a little leaks into the lymph or the blood, and this does not find cells suitable for its multiplication. On the surface, however, there is abundant opportunity for the new brood of virus particles to find fresh cells to infect and in their turn give rise to a new generation. Each generation takes from five to eight hours, and at a guess a cell infected by a single virus particle will give rise to 100 or more descendant particles. By the third or fourth generation the numbers of virus particles are becoming very large and virtually all the cells accessible to the virus are liable to infection. This does not mean that in every case of influenza every lining cell of the air passages is infected. The situation is far too complicated for detailed discussion; all that needs to be grasped is that spread of the virus is over a surface and that there is no significant involvement of cells elsewhere in the body.

The key to the difference between the two types of virus disease is that viruses of the first group with long incubation periods can multiply in a variety of different cells while those like influenza virus in the second group are limited to and specialized for multiplication in one type of superficial cell.

This is a very summary and incomplete account of how viruses multiply in the body. For each well-studied disease some special factors can be recognized which give the disease its particular character, but in hardly any instances can we give adequate reasons for the undue susceptibility of this or that type of cell. The study of the finer chemistry of virus cell interaction will have to go much further before we know for instance why mumps virus attacks the parotid salivary glands or poliomyelitis virus the motor cells of the nervous system.

Symptoms

From the normal medical point of view an infection is important only in proportion to the intensity of the symptoms it produces. The epidemiologist, however, is at least as interested in the person who is infected without symptoms – the 'sub-clinical case' or 'carrier' – as in the manifestly sick patient. One of the most important unsolved problems in virus disease is to know why, of two apparently similar susceptible individuals, infection in one produces symptoms, in the other none.

In discussing how symptoms are produced in typically sick patients we can present a reasonably clear and logical picture that is satisfying and probably almost true. But in doing so we must never forget our ignorance on the all-important matter of the infections that do not produce symptoms.

With this proviso we can make the general statement that when virus multiplication within a cell results in destruction of the cell and liberation of new virus, symptoms result: (*a*) because of loss of the normal function of the cell, (*b*) by the local and general effects of abnormal products from the disintegrating cell.

The most striking symptoms of the first group are those which follow damage to the highly specialized cells of the central nervous system; the muscular paralyses of poliomyelitis are known to everyone. In the second group we have first the local signs of inflammation and second the general 'toxic' effects as especially exemplified in the shivers, rising temperature, headache and loss of appetite that usher in an attack of influenza. There is no evidence that viruses produce any special poisons at all analogous to diphtheria toxin. All that need be postulated is that any disintegrating cell sets free a variety of abnormal and potentially poisonous substances, and that the greater the number of cells involved and the more nearly simultaneous their involvement, the more intense will be the symptoms.

In many ways the situation is analogous to what results from a burn or scald. Heat above a certain degree kills cells and toxic substances are liberated which are responsible for the local redness, swelling and blistering, as well as for the severe symptoms of shock that follow any extensive burn. The tiny blisters of chicken-pox are basically almost the same as the damage produced by a small burn on the skin.

Where one particular part of the body is predominantly affected the local symptoms of virus disease will be almost indistinguishable from those of bacterial infections of the same region. There are several types of conjunctivitis – 'pink eye' – some produced by viruses and some by bacteria. Except for differences of intensity the symptoms are the same for all, redness and irritation, swelling of the soft tissues, excessive secretion of tears and the appearance of pus cells in the fluid. The spots that make up the rashes of smallpox, measles and the rest, each represent the inflammatory reaction produced as a result of virus damage to a little group of cells in the skin. Mumps is mumps because of the swelling and tenderness of the parotid gland that results from virus infection of the glandular cells.

We know rather little about the general symptoms of infection, and I am only moderately sure that the onset of an influenza bout is a reflexion of the extensive and almost simultaneous damage to the lining cells of a considerable portion of the respiratory passages. At the time of writing one of the most exciting fields in medicine is the action of the pituitary hormone A.C.T.H. in dispelling symptoms of this sort, for example in pneumonia. So far there seems to be no 'rhyme or reason' about this action, but it is definite enough to make one chary of discussing the mechanism of symptom production too dogmatically until the work on A.C.T.H. has been properly followed up.

The liberation of virus and its passage to new hosts

The cell destruction that is associated with symptoms in the human patient is also the means by which fresh broods of virus are liberated. The continuing survival of the virus as a species depends on the possibility of some of that virus reaching a new susceptible individual.

Perhaps the simplest type of transfer to understand is that by which the common childhood diseases are spread. We may take German measles as an example. At the time of the skin rash there is also a mild rash on the inside of the mouth and throat from which a large amount of virus enters the saliva and other mouth fluids. Any saliva that leaves the mouth is potentially infectious for others. We know by experiment that if fluid from the throat of a patient with German measles is sprayed into the air from an atomizer susceptible individuals inhaling the mist will contract the disease. Everything points to the accidental inhalation of droplets of infected saliva liberated into the air by coughing, sneezing, or talking as the important mode of natural infection not only in German measles but also for smallpox, chicken-pox, measles, mumps, and influenza. Closely related to droplet infection is the indirect liberation of virus into the air from secretions that have dried on handkerchiefs or bedclothes.

This method of spread by inhalation of droplets or dust particles contaminated with virus is common to many bacterial infections, tuberculosis and diphtheria being two of the most important.

One of the most important developments of public health in the last century has been the virtual elimination of the important bacterial diseases of the intestine, typhoid fever and dysentery, by the development of modern methods of sanitation and sewage disposal. This does not mean, however, that intestinal infections cannot spread in a modern community. Particularly amongst children there will always be occasional opportunities for the transfer of traces of infected excreta to fingers or food. So in the summer we still have outbreaks of diarrhoeal diseases due to bacterial infection and, in addition, we find a similar prevalence of three types of virus infection of the intestinal tract. Curiously none of these viruses gives rise to what the physician normally regards as the standard symptom of intestinal infection – diarrhoea. The first is polio-myelitis virus, the second the virus of infectious jaundice or hepatitis, and the third a group of viruses not yet known to the lay public, the so-called Coxsackie viruses. The recognition of these as essentially intestinal viruses is a recent matter – and one not perhaps acceptable to all authorities. We still have no more than guesses as to what particular cells are infected in the intestine or why in the case of polio and jaundice the virus can sometimes attack the nervous system or the

liver. All that we can feel certain of is that the virus is liberated in the intestine and passes into the environment with
the faeces and that infection of others is by way of faecally-
contaminated material taken in through the mouth. The implications of this point of view for poliomyelitis will need to
be discussed in a special chapter.

The third mode of spread that is sometimes involved in
virus disease is direct infection of minor injuries of the skin.
When we vaccinate against smallpox we deliberately infect
a lightly-scratched area of skin with a virus closely related to
smallpox but causing only a local effect. Simple herpes of the
lips is one condition transmitted naturally in this way, and
there are a few other viruses that fall into the same category.

The last type that needs to be considered is that mediated
by some blood-sucking insect, usually a mosquito. Here we
are particularly liable to meet the additional complication
that the virus in question is really a parasite of monkeys or
birds and is only, as it were, accidentally injected into human
beings. If this is the case, we require to pay much more attention to the natural host than to man if we are to understand
the incidence of the disease. It is clear that, in any mosquito-
borne disease, the virus must multiply in the infected man or
animal and be set free into the blood in sufficient amount and
for sufficient time to give a reasonable chance for other mosquitoes to take up an infected 'meal' of blood and so carry on
the chain of infection. In some instances the transfer by the
insect seems to be a simple mechanical one, but in many cases
the virus also multiplies in the cells of its intermediate insect
host. In yellow fever, for instance, several days must elapse
after the mosquito has taken its meal of infected human blood
before it can convey infection to another susceptible person.
During this period the virus has an opportunity to multiply
in the mosquito and to reach the salivary glands of the insect
in readiness for transfer to a new human host.

Basically, the natural history of a virus disease is similar to that of any other infection, modified only by the strict limitation of the parasite to multiplication within living cells. The key to understanding nearly always lies in the answer to the question – What is the means by which the virus (or, in general, the parasite) persists in nature from generation to generation? When the broad outline of that answer has been obtained, the range of host species involved and the means by which infection passes from one to another, the details of the process can always be worked out for any virus that is conveniently susceptible to laboratory study.

CHAPTER FIVE

IMMUNITY IN VIRUS DISEASE

IN discussing the characteristics of any virus disease of man we shall always have to consider questions of immunity. From time immemorial it has been known that anyone pock-marked by a previous attack of smallpox was quite immune against a second attack. In the eighteenth century in England anyone engaging a domestic servant would insist that she must have passed through the smallpox and so could help in nursing children who might take the disease. Immunity after an attack is not always so complete as it is with smallpox or measles, but even with the common cold there is *some* immunity.

In this chapter we shall be concerned with the basis of this phenomenon of immunity and its general effect on the pattern of infectious disease. It is not a simple matter to condense into a thousand or two words an account of one of the most interesting and complex attributes of the living body. There is a whole science of immunology which at different points is concerned not only with immunity to infection, but also with a variety of other disease conditions, especially the allergic diseases – asthma, hay fever, and the like. It impinges, too, on many other biological sciences, protein chemistry, cellular physiology, and genetics particularly. Its basic concept is that the entry of certain types of foreign material into the body gives rise to the production of substances called antibodies which have a special individual relationship to the material stimulating their production.

These antibodies appear especially in the blood and by suitable physical and chemical methods can be isolated as pure substances. They are proteins extremely similar in general character to one of the proteins of normal blood serum known technically as 'gamma globulin'. This term has now come into general use in connexion with a practical method of preventing measles – a method which, in fact, offers an excellent introduction to the understanding of the significance of antibody in virus disease.

By the time adult life is reached, almost everyone has experienced an attack of measles and is immune to the disease. If blood from, say, fifty donors, is pooled and the liquid serum appropriately treated to give the gamma globulin fraction, this will contain antibodies to measles virus as well as to a great many other viruses and bacteria.

Most parents and doctors feel that if a healthy young school child is exposed to measles, there is nothing to be gained by trying to prevent infection. Provided a doctor is on hand to watch for and deal with any complications like middle-ear infection, the disease presents no danger to a healthy child. But there are often circumstances where it *is* highly desirable to prevent a child from contracting measles from some other member of the family. He may be too young or have some other illness that would be unfavourably influenced by an attack of measles. The standard procedure with such children is to inject a suitable dose of gamma globulin as soon as possible after exposure. In the great majority of cases this will prevent any symptoms of measles.

One can regard the antibody in the blood or in the derived gamma globulin as a substance which very readily and actively attaches itself to the virus particles whenever both are present in the same solution. This union between virus and antibody is essentially a chemical union, but the substances are far too complex to allow any strict chemical formulation of the reaction. For most purposes it is legitimate to think of the two components, virus (or, more generally, *antigen*) and antibody, as analogous to a certain relief pattern, say, that on the face of a coin and a plaster impression from this. When brought together the two patterns fit perfectly and stick tight, but to do this they must be the right patterns. When the measles antibody is injected into the exposed child, it soon reaches the blood, and is there in a position to combine with any measles virus that is not actually inside body cells. When a virus particle is coated or blanketed with attached antibody it is no longer capable of infecting new cells. If it does enter a cell it is mopped up like any inert foreign particle. The net effect of an adequate dose of antibody is that the infection involves only those cells which had already been invaded and goes no further.

From this example we can derive a general picture of the processes of virus immunity. During the primary infection virus and broken-down or incomplete virus products pass to the antibody-producing centres of the body, especially the spleen and lymph glands. There antibody is produced and is liberated into the blood. I shall make no attempt to discuss how antibody is produced, but merely accept the fact of its appearance in the blood and incidentally other tissue fluids in considerable amount. It is a good general rule that antibody is effective against the corresponding virus only when it meets the virus *outside* the cell. A virus particle coated with antibody is non-infective. There are minor qualifications that have to be made; there must obviously be enough antibody to provide an effective coating, and when there is only just enough one may obtain queer variations in results because of the fact that the union of virus and antibody is, like most chemical reactions, to some degree reversible. We find, too, that a mixture of virus and antibody may be inert and neutralized when tested against one type of susceptible animal, but that the same mixture when tested in a very susceptible animal may induce disease. The degree of coating of a virus particle that will render it just non-infective for one type of cell is apparently not enough to prevent it infecting a more susceptible type of cell.

In all experimental work we require methods of measuring (titrating) antibodies, and in principle they usually consist of tests to measure the smallest amount of antibody that will just prevent infection by a standard amount of virus or, if it is more convenient, to find how much virus is just neutralized by a standard amount of serum. If results are to be constant we must also add that the tests must be made in one specified type of animal of such-and-such a size and weight and inoculated in a standard fashion.

In practice this is liable to mean that experiments are complicated and expensive. Suppose we have a serum against one of the viruses which produce brain infection in mice and wish to determine how much antibody it contains in comparison with a standard serum that we know to be effective. The experiment will probably take some such form as this. The experimenter will have stored in a dry ice cabinet a frozen suspension of the brains of 100 mice previously infected with the virus. Portion of this 'stock virus' is thawed out and centrifuged to remove any cells or other solid particles. The solution is now diluted in tenfold steps, $1:10$, 100, $1,000$ and so on to a dilution of 10^9, in some fluid which is known to have no damaging effect on the virus. An equal volume of each dilution is now mixed with an equal volume A – of normal serum known to have no antibody, B – of the serum to be tested, C – of the standard serum known to be rich in antibody. After standing for one hour each mixture is inoculated into the brains of ten mice in a volume of three hundredths of a c.c., the whole experiment calling for 270 mice. The mice, each group of 10 in a separate jar, are watched for 14 days and all deaths recorded. Most of the deaths occur about 6 – 10 days after injection and it is the rule to disregard any deaths before 2 or after 14 days. When the results are tabulated we may find such a result as follows :

VIRUS DILUTIONS

	10¹	10²	10³	10⁴	10⁵	10⁶	10⁷	10⁸	10⁹	Apparent 50% titre
A Normal serum	10/10	10/10	10/10	10/10	10/10	9/9	9/10	6/10	1/10	10⁸·2
B Test serum	10/10	10/10	9/9	10/10	7/10	3/10	0/10	0/10	0/10	10⁵·5
C Standard serum	10/10	4/10	1/10	0/10	0/10	0/8	0/10	0/10	0/10	10²·⁰

Figures show number of deaths / number of mice inoculated.

The accepted unit of virus activity is the amount which when inoculated into each of a large number of animals will kill 50% of them. The 50% titre shown is the number of times the starting material must be diluted, expressed as a power of 10, to reach this level. This allows a direct comparison of the virus content of the various mixtures used.

This result means approximately that there are more than 100 million virus particles in a drop of the stock virus, and second that mixing with serum B allows the inactivation of $10^{2.7}$ (500) virus particles and with serum C $10^{6.2}$ (1,600,000) are inactivated. Actually we cannot legitimately speak of virus particles in experiments of this source; we are dealing only with 'infective units', the relation of which to the number of virus particles will depend on the susceptibility of the animal being used for the test.

Nature of course has no concern with antibody as a means of protecting laboratory mice against experimental infection, but it is only from many quantitative experiments of this type that an understanding of the natural function of antibody has been obtained. Antibody is the means by which the biological requirement of immunity is fulfilled. Let us consider what happens when the child who has had measles is again exposed to infection. Antibody is present in the blood, but there is very little on the surface of the cells in the nose or deeper down the air passages where initiating infection probably occurs. Even in the immune person a few superficial cells are probably infected by virus on each exposure. The virus liberated from such cells cannot, however, continue the sequence that leads to an attack of measles, because at various stages in that sequence virus must pass through blood or other body fluids in order to infect fresh cells. It is at these points of passage that antibody acts, and the total result is the failure of any sign of infection to develop.

Any virus disease, in the course of which virus must at some stage pass through the blood if it is to produce characteristic symptoms, will be one that shows long-lasting or life-long immunity after infection. When, however, symptoms may be produced without passage of virus through the blood immunity is likely to be more transient. The typical example of this condition is to be found in influenza, and its discussion is better left for the chapter on that disease.

We tend to take the fact of immunity for granted as obviously something of biological importance which allows us to get on with our work instead of having monthly or quarterly attacks of this and that disease. Nevertheless, for those with an interest in evolutionary speculation there are some rather subtle problems in understanding why nature adopted this particular solution of the problem of infectious disease. It would be beside the point to attempt a detailed discussion of this sort here. Some of the factors involved are: (1) the multiplicity and variability of potentially parasitic micro-organisms demanding a plastic and adaptive mode of response; (2) the fact that in nature an animal is likely to make first contact with common viruses and other parasites when it is very young. Owing to a combination of circumstances this is in mammals the most favourable time for infection and becomes even more favourable by the fact that maternal antibody is passed to the young before birth and provides a temporary protection; (3) the higher vulnerability of the young adult to first infection by most types of virus, a vulnerability that is most logically counteracted by immunity from infection sustained in early life.

The standard situation, say, in primitive human communities, in regard to very common infections would be that the child is born with antibody derived from the mother's blood. This disappears by about the end of the first year. First infection of the infant probably takes place while there is still some of the mother's antibody in the blood. Both for this reason and because of some intrinsic lower susceptibility of the infant the attack is a mild one. Further, the infant is still completely under its parents' care and will be fed and sheltered during the illness. By the time the child is nearing adult life he should have passed through and developed immunity against all the common infections of his group. There will be infinite variations in the detail of the process and in many individuals the process will fail because of death of the child from first infection. From the evolutionary point of view it is only statistical uniformity that matters and one can see that, broadly speaking, this particular mechanism represents the best available compromise to ensure the persistence of the species in an environment containing numerous micro-organisms of disease themselves evolving under a similar pressure for survival.

When we turn to the pattern of infectious disease as we see it to-day in large human communities the importance of im-munization by natural infection is seen particularly in the different age incidence of different diseases. It will be more convenient to concentrate the discussion of this matter on poliomyelitis where the conditions are such as to show the influence of immunity very clearly. For the present we need only point out that in any *common* disease that is followed by immunity the highest incidence will be at the age where, on the average, children first become exposed to infection. If the virus concerned is liable to be carried by adults the main inci-dence will be around one and two years of age, when mater-nally provided immunity fades, and the child now weaned comes into contact with a contaminated environment. If the virus is not carried by adults and infection is from one child to another the peak of incidence will be in the ages where children mix with those of other families for the first time. Once infection has been overcome immunity is established and the incidence in later ages falls off. The greater the facility for the virus to spread the more rapid will be the falling off of the age incidence curve.

Wherever an infectious disease shows an incidence concentrated either on young adults or on older persons we can be certain that the micro-organism is one which either has not previously been present in the community or is of a type which does not produce immunity. Conversely, if what appears to be a new disease has an age incidence similar to that of measles or infantile paralysis, avoiding adults, we can confidently assume that a less virulent type of the same virus has been widespread in the past.

Immunization against Virus diseases

From the point of view of the doctor concerned not with laboratory problems but with preventing or curing virus disease the most important aspect of modern virology is the possibility of producing immunity by something less than an actual attack of the disease in question. The development of methods of *immunization* against virus diseases was the most important step towards their prevention. It is interesting, too, that the first types of immunization to be developed, inoculation and vaccination against smallpox, were directed against a typical virus disease. Pasteur's most famous work, his method of rabies treatment, was also concerned with a virus disease.

In almost every chapter dealing with a particular virus disease something will need to be said about the possibility of immunization as a means of preventing the disease. In the case of smallpox almost the whole interest of the subject is centred round vaccination, the relation of the vaccine virus to smallpox virus, the history of vaccination and the evidence for its effectiveness. Here it is intended to discuss as far as possible only some of the general aspects of immunization. However, as it is impossible to discuss general principles intelligibly *in vacuo*, examples will need to be given which may have to be referred to again in a slightly different context.

It is worth while first considering for a little what one means by the prevention of an infectious disease. To the ordinary man and the practising doctor it means simply that people in the community no longer get sick and die from that disease. The bacteriologist and the public health administrator know, however, that this result may be reached in two wholly different ways. There has been no yellow fever in Cuba since 1910, although fifty years previously it was notorious for the disease. This change was due to the *elimination* of the virus. In Cuba yellow fever virus passed from man to the *Aedes* mosquito and back to man again. By protecting healthy men from mosquito bite, by preventing access of mosquitoes to patients sick with yellow fever and by diminishing the population of *Aedes* mosquitoes by every available means, the continuing passage of virus from man to mosquito to man became so difficult and uncertain that the virus was rapidly exterminated. But in West Africa, during World War II, American and British troops were free of yellow fever despite the fact that the virus was known to be widely prevalent in the country. They had been protected by immunization so that even if they were bitten by infected mosquitoes any infection was cut short before symptoms could develop.

In the first instance yellow fever was prevented by ridding Cuba completely of the virus, in the second instance by rendering the potential victims insusceptible to the attack of the virus.

As soon as knowledge about any disease reaches the point at which we can begin to think of how it might be prevented, one main question immediately arises. Is it possible to think of eradicating this disease? Can we by appropriate measures ever hope to kill and finally eliminate every single virus particle in the country? If it can be done it is nearly always worth attempting. In Western civilized countries most of the great plagues of the past have been actually eliminated in this literal fashion. In England there is no plague, cholera, typhus, smallpox, or malaria – apart from the occasional patient who has been infected abroad. All these at one time or another have been major causes of death.

There are a few general rules about the elimination of micro-organisms. If at some stage the germ must pass through some other animal in order to continue to survive, the chances of elimination are likely to depend almost wholly on how readily that animal transfer can be stopped. Typhus was eliminated by getting rid of body lice, plague by an attack on rats and fleas. Malaria disappeared from England mainly because of the progressive diminution in the extent of mosquito-breeding swamps. When there is fairly direct transfer of infection from person to person it is often possible to eliminate a disease if two criteria are fulfilled: (1) The disease always, or virtually always, takes on an easily recognized form; (2) it is regarded as being so dangerous that the public will submit to the necessary inconveniences of quarantine and compulsory treatment.

We could eliminate measles if we wished, simply by the segregation from all other children for three weeks of every contact of a measles case. It would be an extremely expensive matter, but I have no doubt that, given the demand and public acquiescence in the measure needed, it would be physically possible to do so. In fact, of course, no one is sufficiently interested in, or afraid of, measles to ask for any such effort.

On the other hand, the public generally in America, New Zealand, and Australia is very conscious of the danger of poliomyelitis, at least during an epidemic, and would almost certainly submit to measures believed capable of eliminating the disease. Here, however, we know that for every manifest case of paralysis there are ten or a thousand others without paralysis who are also just as capable of disseminating the virus. In every disease where there are a considerable number of subclinical infections – where the virus can multiply and be liberated without producing symptoms – it is impossible to think of eliminating the disease by any form of quarantine action or compulsory treatment.

Where it is clear that we have to continue to live with a disease-producing germ, whether it is a virus or anything else, then efforts at preventing the disease should logically take the form of trying to ensure that the largest possible proportion of infections should be subclinical. Perhaps it would be more correct to say that our object should be to replace natural immunization in which we will always have a certain ratio of subclinical infections to definite illnesses and to deaths by an artificial method of immunization which produces no more than an occasional mild illness and no deaths.

The discovery of the new antibiotic drugs, like penicillin, gives another approach to the prevention of diseases whose agents cannot be exterminated. At least one of the venereal diseases can be prevented with certainty by a single injection of penicillin soon after exposure to infection. Malaria in the South-west Pacific theatre of war was effectively prevented by the daily dose of atebrin, or in the last month or two by the weekly dose of paludrine. So far there has been no drug discovered that has any specific action on a virus comparable to the action of penicillin on the streptococcus of 'blood-poisoning' or of paludrine on the malaria parasite. Until some such specific is obtained the sole approach to the prevention of the common virus diseases will remain by immunization.

From what has been said about the nature of immunity to virus diseases it will be clear that to be successful any method of artificial immunization must be able to provoke the production of antibody of the same quality as that induced by natural infection and in sufficient amount. There are three ways in which this can be attempted. The first is to produce an infection by the virus that causes the natural disease but to administer it in some way less likely to produce severe illness. The first of all attempts at immunization was the 'inoculation' against smallpox brought to England from the Middle East in the early eighteenth century. Inoculation into the skin of pus from a mild case of natural smallpox very often produced a milder illness than one contracted in the course of nature. The method is not currently applied to any human disease, but it has been suggested that it would be advisable to see that at some time before she was eighteen every girl had been infected with german measles on the ground that it is then a harmless disease and will produce immunity against infection at the only time when there is real danger, that is, during pregnancy. Poultry farmers make important use of the method in immunizing chickens against laryngotracheitis. This is a disease somewhat analogous in its symptoms to the laryngeal form of diphtheria that kills by blocking the windpipe. If chicks are infected by a swab in the vent a harmless local infection is produced that protects against infection in the air passages.

The second method is also to infect with a living virus, but a virus which has a much lower virulence than the natural cause of the disease. Vaccination against smallpox is the classical example, but in some ways immunization against yellow fever gives a clearer picture of the process by which such methods are developed.

All viruses are capable of variation, and many of the changing characteristics of the diseases they produce result from this capacity to mutate. In viruses we see essentially the same processes of reproduction, mutation, and survival that make up evolution in higher forms, but here the process is speeded up enormously, and if we wish we can see changes accomplished in a week that would take a million years in a mammalian species. Mutation in many directions is always occurring, and with any change in the environment, for example when we transfer a virus from man to mouse or chick embryo, some new variant is likely to replace the former standard type as the predominant form in the new population. In general the virulence of a virus for man is reduced by growing it for many generations in the cells of some other animal. This depends simply on the fact that when variants are automatically selected for ability to grow in the new host it is likely that they will concomitantly lose some of their capacity to grow in the old host. Fortunately it is the rule that changes in what we call the antigenic character of the virus rarely accompany changes in virulence, that is to say the quality of the antibody produced is not usually altered. The general procedure in seeking an 'attenuated' variant of a virus for immunization, then, is to transfer the virus from a human case to some animal in which it does not grow very readily. It is transferred successively in the new host until it can multiply freely and is then carefully tested to see whether a satisfactory loss of virulence has occurred. In the case of yellow fever the virus was first transferred to monkeys, in which it produces a disease very similar to the human one, then to mice, and finally to tissue culture. In tissue cultures we have fragments of tissue kept at body heat in a complex solution designed to be as close to the tissue fluids of the body as possible. Most of the cells in such cultures are living, particularly when, as is the case with the yellow fever experiments, the tissues come from chick embryos. The virus will multiply readily, and if a mutant is present specially suited to grow in this way it will overgrow the others and come out on top. In Dr Max Theiler's tissue cultures of yellow fever a mutant called 17D came to dominate the picture. It had a much diminished virulence for mice and monkeys and was found to provide a near-perfect agent for immunization of human beings against yellow fever.

The third method is to use not a living virus which can multiply and produce more virus in the body, but the dead bodies of virus particles in sufficient amount to act as an adequate stimulus for antibody production. The requirements are that the method used for killing the virus should not modify its antibody-producing quality and that it is possible to obtain enough actual virus material by a commercially practical technique. Theoretically this is the ideal method, but only two virus vaccines of this type have been prepared and used successfully against human disease. Influenza vaccines have been in use since 1943, and in 1954 the U.S. Armed Services accepted annual immunization against influenza as a standard procedure. The virus is readily obtained by chick embryo culture in a sufficiently concentrated form for use as a killed vaccine. The Salk polio vaccine is prepared from virus grown in tissue culture and killed with formalin. In mid 1954 it was undergoing its first large-scale test in the United States. The great advantage of these killed virus vaccines is that in killing the virus one also kills any other unwanted virus that may have found its way in by accident of one sort or another.

There is a fourth and final method of immunization which may eventually be used against poliomyelitis, but so far is confined to the prevention of some virus diseases of domestic animals. The person or animal to be protected is first given a dose of antibody in the form of serum from a recovered individual and under the protection of this a dose of virus. The amount of virus must be such that it is not quite completely neutralized by the antibody. It should produce no symptoms, but multiply sufficiently to produce fresh antibody that will provide a persisting immunity long after the injected serum has been eliminated.

Which method will be used in any given situation will depend on many circumstances. Quite often the decision will depend simply on the particular interests of the virologist who first undertakes the task. Whatever the choice, there will be difficulties to be overcome, and, once anyone has gone through to a successful result, his method will probably remain the basis of any future developments.

Two final reservations should be made about immunizations against virus diseases. The first is that we can never expect 100 per cent success from any preventive measure. Human beings differ enormously in their susceptibility to infection and in the readiness with which they respond with antibody production to the appropriate stimulus. In some virus diseases there are many different 'strains' of the virus in circulation, and immunization with some particular vaccine may be much more effective against one strain than against another. Vaccines are made and administered by people who are as subject to occasional lapses from care and common sense as other people, and persons ostensibly immunized may have been given an inactive vaccine. All these more or less accidental factors make it necessary always to seek adequate statistical proof that a given method does actually protect. It is just as foolish to condemn a method because of a few known failures to protect as to acclaim it as successful because of a few instances of apparent protection.

The second reservation is that where a natural disease does not produce immunity to a second attack we cannot expect to obtain protection by any form of immunization. There may turn out to be exceptions to this rule in the future, but for the present it stands. That is one of the reasons why I am completely sceptical about the likelihood that isolation of the common cold virus would lead to a method of preventing colds. It is not easy to do a great deal better than Nature.

CHAPTER SIX

HERPES SIMPLEX

NEXT to the common cold there is probably no commoner or more trivial ailment than simple herpes of the lips. There are many people who with every cold develop a blister or two on the lips, which soon break down to give a sore-crusted patch that usually heals completely in a few days. If they suffer a more serious fever, such as pneumonia, the herpes blisters tend to be more extensive and disfiguring. Some particularly sensitive individuals can expect a crop of blisters with every exposure to a cold wind or an undue amount of sunshine. The most characteristic thing about simple herpes irrespective of the severity of its manifestations is its recurrent quality. Anyone who suffers from herpes can expect to continue having attacks, usually on the same area of the skin of the lips and provoked by the same sort of circumstances, for the rest of his life. Not infrequently one comes across a person subject to attacks of herpes in more unusual situations, the front of the eye, a finger, the lobe of the ear. With these, too, the rule holds that the attacks are recurrent and at each recurrence involve the same area of the body surface.

Now this behaviour does not in any way resemble that of a typical infectious disease. It seems clear that the process is initiated from inside the body. There is an unduly sensitive area of the skin which, under the stimulus of some rise in body temperature or of some external irritation, breaks down into a trivial sore and then undergoes rapid repair. There is no suggestion whatever that at each attack a micro-organism is transferred from someone else and initiates a blister which on breaking transfers infected fluid to another victim. It was, therefore, extremely surprising to bacteriologists when about 1912 it was shown that fluid from a herpes blister could quite regularly produce a typical disease in rabbits and that the agent responsible had all the characteristics of a typical virus. For the rabbit it is in fact a rather dangerous virus.

The simplest way of showing its activity is to anaesthetize the front of a rabbit's eye with cocaine or the like and gently scratch the surface through a drop of fluid from a herpes blister. In two days' time tiny little mounds will be seen developing on the eye, and in another day or two the eye will be found to show fairly severe inflammation with a good deal of pus. If the eye is washed out with saline, and, after appropriate manipulations, the fluid filtered through one of the membranes used to eliminate bacteria, it is found that the filtrate can produce exactly the same effect in another rabbit. This transference from one animal to another can be continued indefinitely. The infection in the rabbit at least is a typical virus disease and can be studied by all the standard methods of virology. In my own laboratory it is regarded as the 'best' virus on which a beginner in the science can cut his teeth. It is virtually harmless to human beings; it can be isolated with ease, if not from the student himself, at least from one of his friends; and in its own particular fashion it provides examples of all the typical phenomena of virus disease. It is for the same reason that this insignificant condition is given pride of place in this book as the first human virus disease to be discussed in some detail.

Suppose we start with a small amount of fluid pricked from a couple of early blisters on the lip and mix this with some saline solution containing enough penicillin to destroy the activity of any bacteria that may be present. For most

work with herpes virus it is desirable to use the chick embryo rather than the rabbit, and the first step is to deposit
this penicillin-treated fluid on the outer membrane, the
chorioallantois, of several chick embryos. The technique
is the very simple one that was described in the second
chapter. The virus is spread over a square inch or two of
the sensitive membrane, the hole in the eggshell is closed,
and the embryo put back in an incubator to continue its
development for two or three days. Then we break away
the shell and cut out carefully the area of the membrane on
which the virus was deposited. Over its surface will be seen
a variable number of white opaque nodules. Each of these
nodules – we usually refer to them as pocks – represents the
point at which a single virus unit penetrated and infected
one of the surface cells of the egg membrane. It multiplied
inside the cell and at the same time so damaged the cell that
substances diffused out of it which caused surrounding cells
to start growing and dividing more rapidly than normal.
These surrounding cells were then infected by the 'crop' of
virus units from the central cell. The process continued,
cell proliferation preceding infection outward from the centre,
so that in two days' time there were sufficient cells, many
damaged by virus, at each point to produce a pock easily
visible to the naked eye.

If each pock corresponds as we have assumed to the point
at which a single virus unit initiated infection, it is obvious
that this method gives us a method of measuring the number
of infectious units, of active virus particles, in any given
material. This is the pock-counting method of virus titra-
tion. In most experiments with herpes virus we need a stock
preparation with the largest convenient amount of virus. A
number of egg membranes thickly covered with an almost
confluent mass of infected cells forms the usual starting
material. The membranes are ground to a smooth paste and

suspended in a few cc. of some simple fluid like bacteriological broth. This is centrifuged and the deposit of cell
fragments discarded. We now make a series of accurate tenfold dilutions and place a measured amount of each diluted
virus on the membranes of a fresh series of chick embryos.
Two days later we look at the membranes and count the
number of pocks. The fluid diluted 1:100 will give membranes too thickly covered with opacities to be counted, but
we shall probably find that at 1:10,000 or 1:100,000 we
obtain satisfactory numbers. If six eggs have been used for
each dilution the membranes might show numbers like the
following :

1:10,000	..	55	60	62	30	57	10
1:100,000	..	7	8	5	5	2	2

From this, by allowing for the volume of fluid placed on each
membrane, we can calculate that each cc. of the original
material had about $6 \times 10^5 \times 20 = 1.2 \times 10^7$ infective units
per cc. There are many technical points that must be care-
fully watched if accurate measurements of this sort are
to be made, but the principle of the method is perfectly
simple.

The next step towards the experimental understanding of
the natural history of herpes requires the testing of blood-
serum from various individuals for the presence or absence
of antibody to the virus. In any laboratory one will find a
few people who often have herpes, others who are quite
certain that whether they have colds or pneumonia, whether
they spend the winter ski-ing or sunbathe in summer, they
never have herpes. We take a sample of blood from one or
more individuals of each group and separate the liquid
serum from the clot of blood cells. Our aim is to determine
whether the serum has the property of neutralizing or

inactivating the virus. If the serum is mixed with the virus will it prevent infection of the sensitive cells of the egg membrane? The technique is again very simple in principle, with certain practical refinements which need not be considered here. We dilute our stock virus so that a standard amount would give 200 to 300 pocks on the membrane. We mix this dilution of virus with an equal volume of serum and put the mixture on the egg membranes in the usual way. Almost always we get one of two clear-cut answers. If the serum is from a person who has never had herpes the membrane will be covered with the expected 100–150 pocks. If it is from someone subject to herpes attacks there will be no foci on the membrane. This 'all-or-nothing' result is characteristic of human sera. If we take serum from the same person a year or two later the same result will obtain as for the first sample. If for the time being we confine ourselves to adults and older children we can divide all of them into two groups, herpetics and non-herpetics. The relative size of the two groups in different circumstances is a matter of great interest that we can discuss later, but for the moment the important point is that by and large all adults remain indefinitely in their category.

The next step in our retracing of the experimental course by which the natural history of herpes was unravelled is to visit any large orphanage containing a hundred or so toddlers between one and two years. It will be most unusual to fail to find one or two children suffering from what is medically known as acute aphthous stomatitis. What we see is simply a moderately sick irritable child dribbling from a sore mouth. If the mouth is carefully examined, either blisters or raw areas often yellow with secondary infection where blisters have broken will be seen on various parts of the mucous lining of the mouth. Quite often there are extensions of the ulceration on the lips. In the great majority of instances this represents a *first* infection with the virus of herpes. The virus can easily be picked up on a cotton wool swab and shown to be present by the same sort of tests that are used to isolate the virus from adult herpes blisters.

There is, however, one very important difference from an attack of herpes in an adult. At the time of the illness the child with the acute mouth infection has no antibody in his blood. Three weeks later the ulceration in the mouth will have healed and the toddler will be happy again. Now a fresh blood sample will show plenty of antibody capable of neutralizing the herpes virus. This production of antibody is, of course, a response to first infection with the virus. As far as present knowledge goes the child once infected with herpes will remain infected for life and will always show antibody in his blood. He will be subject to recurrent herpes, but no one can prophesy how frequent or infrequent it will be.

On the other hand, if a child escapes primary infection with herpes virus until it is five years old it is unlikely to be infected subsequently and will neither suffer from recurrent herpes nor develop antibody.

This outline of the experimental approach to the study of herpes is enough to show how an intelligible picture of the natural history of the disease can be built up. A Melbourne epidemiologist, Dr S. G. Anderson, a few years ago made a special study of how infection with herpes virus spread amongst the children in an orphanage. The babies came into the institution soon after birth, usually with their mothers. About the age of eight months they were transferred to a few large wards where they remained until they were two years old. While in these wards all the infants became infected with herpes, about half of them with manifest signs of sore mouth and salivation, the others without any noticeable symptoms. The fact of infection in these was established by the appearance of antibody in their blood about the same time as other children were showing the signs of typical sore-mouth infection. There was no difficulty at all in seeing how infection was spread. Children of that age are always putting things in their mouths and dribbling saliva. There is a very free commerce in saliva amongst any group of crawlers and toddlers. If one of them has a primary herpes infection of the mouth the virus will certainly be liberally dispersed over every movable object in the nursery. Herpes is not a highly infectious disease, and for implantation to occur it is probable that contaminated material must make direct contact with some little cut or abrasion on the tongue, gums, or inside the cheek. Such minor injuries must be very common where children are not under constant supervision and in the orphanage all became infected.

There was one particularly interesting feature of these orphanage infections. Although the children entered a highly contaminated environment when they were eight or nine months old, they did not contract the infection till they were more than eleven months old. Dr Anderson's interpretation was that nearly all these children received from their mothers a temporary resistance against infection. Any antibody in the mother's blood passes into the baby's and both antibody and the corresponding resistance to infection gradually disappear within the first year of the infant's life. In very young babies the blood does contain measurable antibody against herpes, and this antibody disappears after six months. The resistance against infection seems to last a little longer.

Anybody who has read this discussion closely will probably see that there is a serious difficulty here. We speak of babies being resistant to infection because they have antibody in their blood, but we have previously spoken of people who always have antibody in their blood, yet suffer recurrent attacks of herpes. The difference is a very important one, with a crucial bearing on the problems of how immunity develops after an attack of a virus disease.

In the young infant who has never been infected by the virus, but whose blood contains antibody from the mother, infection with herpes must come from outside. We can imagine a little crack on the gum where a toy has been chewed too hard, and herpes virus from some other child's saliva entering the damaged region. In the tiny wound there will be a small leak of serum (and antibody) from the blood. If this reacts with the virus the mixture loses its power to infect the damaged tissues just as it fails to infect the egg membrane in our experiments. It is only when the amount of antibody in the blood falls below an effective level – somewhere around the child's first birthday – that virus can initiate infection in some area of minor damage to the tissues.

In the adult, who ever since he recovered from his primary herpes infection in infancy has been having occasional cold sores on his lips, the conditions are quite different. At the time of the primary infection some of the surface cells (epidermis) of the skin of the lips were involved without being destroyed. In some way they had become tolerant of or resistant to the virus. These skin cells and their descendants remained infected, but for the most part they gave no evidence of the action of the virus. As most people know, the surface cells of the skin are constantly being replaced from below. There is a deeper layer of actively growing cells, the progeny of which, as they approach the surface, become harder and drier and are eventually discarded. In the areas of the lip that are infected with herpes virus we assume that in the basal actively growing skin cells the virus is multiplying, but at almost exactly the same rate as the cells themselves multiply. There is antibody in the blood which can prevent passage of the virus to distant cells, but the blood serum and its antibody can make no contact with the inside of a cell. If a virus is actually inside a cell it cannot be influenced by antibody circulating in the blood. This is a very important generalization that must be borne in mind in thinking about any question of immunity to viruses.

The herpes virus then is existing in these cells in a delicate state of equilibrium, its rate of growth exactly adjusted to that of the cell. With a relatively minor change, e.g. in the body temperature, this equilibrium is disturbed and the virus takes control. Multiplication occurs. The cells are damaged and destroyed and the typical blisters form. Still the antibody in the blood plays no part. The virus quiescent and active has remained throughout within the cells out of contact with antibody. As the cells break down and inflammatory changes appear, virus is liberated and probably the mild, circumscribed character of most herpes sores is due to the fact that any spread of infection by liberated virus is stopped by the antibody that is always present in the blood. With each attack of herpes there is enough virus set free to act as a fresh stimulus to antibody production. So it results that all persons subject to herpes have antibody in their blood. The best way, in fact, of telling whether a given individual is or is not infected is to make the appropriate blood test – if his blood 'neutralizes' herpes virus then he is a carrier of herpes virus and potentially subject to recurrent herpes.

The changing incidence of herpes

Just before the outbreak of World War II we were very interested in the potentialities that had appeared with the development of the very simple way of testing blood serum for herpes virus antibody on the chick embryo. We wanted to see how many people were subject to herpes and how many had escaped infection completely. As is usually the case in such investigations, our first extensive tests were made on random

samples of serum from hospital patients. Every day any
hospital laboratory receives dozens of samples of blood for
tests of one sort or another. It is usual to find that after the
test required by the patient's doctor has been completed there
is sufficient blood or serum left over to allow a test for herpes
antibody to be done. So in a few weeks it is possible to accumulate results from large numbers of people with a variety of
minor and major illnesses, but all from patients visiting a
public hospital and, therefore, from the lower economic
groups of the community. Around a hospital laboratory there
are also to be found considerable numbers of University
graduates in medicine and science who have no objection to
providing a sample of blood for any reasonable purpose.
Even in Australia the great majority of these people come
from families at a higher economic level than the average
hospital patient.

When the tests were analysed there was a striking difference
between the two groups. Public hospital patients nearly all
gave evidence of herpes infection. The results were practically
the same (between 90 and 95 per cent) whether the sera were
from adults attending the Royal Melbourne Hospital or from
children (other than babies) at the Children's Hospital. In the
group of higher economic level, however, the proportion was
only 37 per cent.

After the war, in 1947–8, a similar survey was undertaken
in Melbourne, but this time attention was concentrated on
children. Blood serum was obtained from 100 children attending private schools, i.e. from families of higher economic
status, and from 100 Children's Hospital patients. This time
the first group gave almost exactly the same figure – just under 40 per cent – as was obtained previously, but the public
hospital children gave only 55 per cent of sera with herpes
antibody.

. Now this seems to us a most interesting relationship

between economic status and the incidence of an infectious disease. Perhaps it would be advisable to wait until similar studies can be made in other countries than Australia before being too dogmatic about the interpretation of the results. At present our interpretation of the situation in Australia must be something like this. If a parent is subject to herpes he or she will at irregular intervals be liberating rather large amounts of virus on to handkerchiefs, eating utensils, and so forth. When no particular care is taken over the baby's diet and feeding habits infection is bound to involve him. On the other hand, where care is taken to sterilize plates, bottles, spoons and so forth, and where parents are consciously trying to minimize opportunities of conveying infection to the infant, it seems to be relatively easy to prevent an infant contracting primary herpes. In Melbourne there has in the last two decades been a steady increase in the facilities for advice on child care and in the use made of these facilities. The fall in the incidence of herpes in the general child population can, we think, be regarded as a rather direct index of the success that has been obtained in inculcating hygienic methods of child feeding. I do not know of any other equally objective method of measuring success in this respect, and perhaps I can be pardoned for suggesting that any organization interrested in the hygiene of childhood that wishes to know how its work is succeeding should have similar surveys done every five years or so.

The evolutionary aspect

So far we have been concerned only with herpes as it affects a modern civilized community. It is a very trivial disease which, in unsophisticated people, involves almost everyone. Yet from the point of view of the virus that causes it this situation must be regarded as an extremely successful one. What more, we might say, can a virus ask for when it affects almost every individual of its host species in a way that ensures a succession of fresh opportunities to pass to the next generation of hosts? There is no reason to doubt that herpes has been a minor nuisance to the human race throughout its history. I think we can see a clear reference to herpes of the lips in *Romeo and Juliet*. When Mercutio speaks of Mab, the fairy queen, he tells of how she runs

> *O'er ladies' lips who straight on kisses dream*
> *Which oft the angry Mab with blisters plagues*
> *Because their breaths with sweet meats tainted are.*

If we look back on human evolution we come not so very long ago to the stage in which men probably lived in bands of a few dozen to a hundred individuals with very little contact with others of their species. Under such circumstances there would be little or no opportunity for the spread and persistence of a disease like measles. Herpes, however, could obviously persist from generation to generation in a way impossible for any virus that produces only a short-lasting disease and then vanishes. The infant can be infected by its mother and twenty years later it will still be liberating virus which will infect his or her own infant. Here, then, is one virus disease which might well have lived along with the human species since the days of its monkeyhood.

There are two sets of facts which suggest that this is literally true. In the first place, many epidemiologists agree that whenever two species live together as host and parasite for very long periods the processes of mutual adaptation result in the disease becoming milder, in the sense of rarely producing death or serious disability, but still retaining the power to be freely transferred to other host individuals. This is so beautifully exemplified in herpes that we must assume that the association between man and the virus is a very old one indeed. There is, of course, no way of discovering directly whether herpes of the lips affected prehistoric man or his more ape-like ancestors. At least one Egyptian mummy is known whose skin shows blobs which probably mean that this particular man died of smallpox, and perhaps in some well-preserved mummy herpes blisters might be observed, but we cannot hope to go further back than that.

It would, however, be rather strong indirect evidence if we could find that monkeys were also subject to herpes or at least were infected with some virus so similar to herpes that we should have to postulate a single ancestral virus that attacked the remote common ancestor of monkeys, apes, and men. There is, in fact, a monkey virus which is very similar to herpes virus in all but one vital point. It produces almost the same effect as herpes virus in rabbits and chick embryos, it is inactivated almost as completely by herpes antibody, and it produces the same fine structural changes in the cells that it infects. The outstanding difference from herpes is that it gives rise to a highly fatal human disease.

In 1930 an American bacteriologist was examining a monkey being used for research on poliomyelitis when the animal bit him in the hand. The wound was cleaned up and nothing unusual was observed for a day or two. Then a crop of blisters not unlike those of herpes formed at the edge of the bite and the patient became feverish. The illness progressed, and before long there were signs that the spinal cord was involved, first with paralysis of the lower half of the body. Then the paralysis gradually spread upwards and the patient died. A virus was isolated from the blisters on the wound, and, after death, from the spinal cord.

It seemed certain that this virus came from the monkey's saliva just as herpes virus will be found in the saliva of a person who has had an active herpes sore on his lip. At least two other cases of this sort of death from monkey bite have been recorded, and when blood samples from a large number of monkeys were tested a large proportion showed power to neutralize the virus. Just as in human beings this means that at some time or other they had been infected with what we can reasonably call monkey herpes. No one has made a really comprehensive study of the condition in monkeys – after all, monkey bite is not one of the normal perils of human existence – and any conclusions must be somewhat tentative. My own conclusion from these experiments was simply that the monkey virus and the human virus have gradually diverged from a common ancestral type as the two evolutionary lines leading to man and monkey went their different ways. To a biologist interested in the relationship between host and parasite the most illuminating feature of the situation is the fact that each of the viruses has remained almost harmless to its natural host. That is the inevitable result of mutual adaptation between host and virus. But when a virus is transferred to an unnatural host a new series of adaptations must begin if the virus is to persist. Often, as in the case of monkey herpes in man, the virus may be too virulent; on the other hand, human herpes fails to infect monkeys at all. They have now diverged too far to flourish on any but their natural hosts.

CHAPTER SEVEN

POLIOMYELITIS

DURING the 1880s there were recognized in Sweden epidemics of a disease in which young children became paralysed in one or more limbs. Occasional cases had been seen in various countries during the earlier part of the nineteenth century, and from the microscopic changes present in the spinal cord the name 'acute anterior poliomyelitis' had been given to the disease. Not until the Swedish epidemics, however, was there any clear indication that the disease was an infectious one. Since then epidemics of 'polio' have become almost progressively more frequent and more widespread over the globe. To-day poliomyelitis is the most important of the virus diseases of civilized countries and one that, up to 1954, had resisted all attempts at its control. Almost alone amongst infectious diseases, polio had failed to wilt and disappear under the combined impact of an improving standard of living and active public health measures. In fact, the history of poliomyelitis suggests inescapably that the incidence of poliomyelitis *increases* concomitantly with improvement in the standard of living and of personal hygiene. It was becoming increasingly evident that some means of vaccination or immunization was urgently needed if we were to control the disease. At the time of writing, October, 1954, the world is awaiting the results of a very large scale test of the effectiveness of the Salk polio vaccine in protecting children against paralysis. There is a high expectation amongst virologists that the vaccine will prove successful.

Polio is not an easy disease to understand in any circumstances, and this paradox of its being favoured by the conditions which we know diminish the incidence of all ordinary infections is not an easy one to accept. I have felt therefore that it is necessary to make a serious attempt to describe the situation in regard to poliomyelitis and to give a little more technical detail than would be appropriate in regard to other diseases.

In 1909 it was shown that the spinal cord of a child dead of infantile paralysis contained a virus which on inoculation into the brain of a monkey would provoke a similar often fatal disease. The virus multiplied in the monkey and by inoculation of suitable extracts of nervous tissue could be passed indefinitely from animal to animal. The study of the viruses concerned with polio has gone on continuously since 1909 and we now know a great deal about them and the disease that they cause in experimentally infected animals. Without going into the stages by which the knowledge was obtained we can outline present knowledge about the polio viruses as follows: Polio may be due to any one of three related viruses, one of which is very much commoner at present than either of the other two. All three are termed poliomyelitis viruses and are given names derived from the particular 'strain' of virus taken as the type for each group. They are differentiated by their immunological behaviour, i.e. if a monkey recovers from infection with the common type 'Brunhilde' he will be immune to any other Brunhilde type virus, but he will be paralysed by a virus of either 'Lansing' or 'Leon' type. There is one other important difference in regard to the range of animals that can be experimentally infected. All types will infect monkeys and chimpanzees, but only viruses of Lansing type can be trained to infect small rodents including white mice. In their other known characteristics all polio viruses are similar. They are extremely small, approximately 1/100 the diameter of an ordinary bacterium like a staphylococcus and only about 1/1,000,000 of its mass. They are relatively resistant to damage by heat or chemicals. This makes it easy to isolate the virus if it is present in sewage or other material containing very large numbers of bacteria. The bacteria can be killed with a mild antiseptic like ether without damage to the virus and the material then inoculated into monkeys. If paralysis is produced, if the microscopic changes are of standard type, and if the infection can be transferred to another monkey, we can record the *isolation* of the virus.

The way in which paralysis is produced either in the naturally infected child or in the inoculated monkey is very easily grasped by anyone with some elementary knowledge of the physiology of muscular action. Put very briefly and dogmatically, all voluntary movements depend on nervous impulses coming to the muscles from cells in the central part of the spinal cord. All sorts of higher-level processes are also involved in producing the pattern of the movement desired, but the final 'orders' to the muscles are all from these so-called 'motor cells of the anterior horn'. The polio virus multiplies with particular ease in these cells if it can reach them. As in other examples of virus multiplication the cell concerned is liable to be destroyed or grossly damaged and loses its normal functional activities. There is a regular relationship between the position of the nerve cells and the muscles they control. Arm muscles, for instance, are controlled by spinal cord cells at neck level, while the control of the legs is by cells about 12 inches lower down the cord. Whenever a sufficient proportion of the cells related to a given muscle group is destroyed by the virus, weakness or complete paralysis will be observed in that group.

Perhaps the clearest indication of the relation of the virus to the disease can be obtained from investigations made by Drs Sabin and Ward in Cincinnati, on where the virus could be found in the bodies of children dead of poliomyelitis. They showed that in the nervous system there was virus associated with the nerve cells that govern muscular movement both in the brain proper and in the spinal cord, but little or none in other parts of the brain. There was no virus in nerves or paralysed muscles and none in the blood or the main viscera. Elsewhere than in the nervous system the virus was limited to the alimentary tract. It could be found in the throat, in the wall of the intestine and in large amount in the contents of the intestine. The large amount of polio virus that is excreted in the faeces is probably the most important single fact for the interpretation of the disease. Most modern studies of polio epidemics use as their raw material information as to the proportion of adult and child contacts from whose faeces virus can be isolated. Virus can almost always be isolated with ease from the faeces of patients. Particularly striking is the fact that in the polio season virus can be isolated from a cubic centimetre or two of the mixed sewage of any large American city in which polio is prevalent.

Largely as a result of such studies we can state the second outstanding fact in the relationship between the virus and the disease – *most children who become infected with and excrete the virus show no evidence of paralysis* and only occasionally present minor symptoms due to the infection, such as fever and headache. The paralysis that defines the disease is, even in a severe epidemic, a relatively rare result of infection by the virus. One might well claim that the main practical problem in poliomyelitis is to know what determines why this minority of infections is followed by paralysis. If all infections by the virus conformed to the non-paralytic character of the great majority, polio would present no problem at all. Unfortunately paralysis does occur. In some individuals virus multiplication in the throat or bowel allows spread to the central nervous system as well as liberation of virus into the bowel contents. It is still not certain how the virus reaches the spinal cord; one group of investigators think that it passes up the nerves, another that it travels by the blood. Even when virus has reached the nervous system it may give evidence of its presence, e.g. by the child having a stiff neck and a head-ache, yet not produce paralysis. It seems that there are many difficulties in the way of the polio virus reaching the special motor cells where it multiplies most readily and by whose destruction paralysis results. We can at present only look at the results of infection from a statistical point of view. We know that the *probability* of severe paralysis may be increased by a number of factors –

(1) The type of virus responsible for the current epidemic. Some epidemics obviously produce a much higher ratio of paralytic to non-paralytic infections than others, and we can relate this only to differences in the invasiveness of the viruses themselves.

(2) The age of the person infected. Age has two aspects – the older the person the more likely is he to be immunized by past experience of infection, but if an individual has had no previous contact with poliomyelitis there is much to suggest that he becomes progressively more liable to paralysis when he *is* infected at least up to the age of twenty or twenty-five years.

(3) Transient vulnerability of the motor nerve cells. There is good evidence that over-exertion at the time invasion of the nervous system is occurring will tend towards an increased degree of paralysis of the muscles involved. It is also established that various types of injury, including such things as a broken limb, operative removal of tonsils, or an immunizing injection may be followed by localization of paralysis to a corresponding region. It is by no means clear how these results ensue, but the facts are on record, and we must assume that in some way the nerve cells concerned are rendered unduly vulnerable to attack by the virus.

All three points will be found to be of importance when we come to discuss what can be *done* about poliomyelitis.

Age and poliomyelitis

Anyone with an interest in poliomyelitis and some knowledge of its modern type must wonder why its 'popular'
name used to be infantile paralysis. In America, England, and
Australia nowadays babies are little affected; the incidence
is largely on the young school child between five and ten,
with an increasing number of older children and adults.
Before about 1916, however, there was real justification for
the use of the word infantile; all the old epidemics showed a
concentration of paralysis in infants, i.e. children under five
years of age. Some recent epidemics such as those in Malta,
1943, and Israel, 1950, have again shown this old infantile
pattern. These two types of age pattern with main incidence
on the young school child and the infant respectively are
not the only forms that can be taken by polio epidemics.
When we hear of the first epidemic of poliomyelitis to be
reported from some Pacific island or from some Arctic community we nearly always find that the greatest toll of paralysis and death is on the adolescent and adult. Infants and
young children characteristically escape the most lightly.

There is obviously something of very great interest in
these variations in the incidence of disease according to age,
and in order to discuss their significance it is first necessary
to say something about how the age incidence of a disease
is measured and expressed. The simplest procedure is to take
the records of an outbreak in a given city and tabulate in
five-year age groups the number of individuals paralysed
and the number of deaths. The total number is thus broken
down into percentages in each five-year age group and a
block diagram prepared. For most purposes this is all that
is required. Sometimes, however, we have to deal with communities in which there is an abnormal distribution of ages.
We can get a satisfactory comparison of the age incidence of

polio in the Armed Services with that in the civilian population only if we calculate the actual proportion of cases in
each age group. If, for instance, we have ten cases of polio
in a population of 83,000 infants 0–5 years old we will
record this as a rate of 12 per 100,000. When such a corrected
age incidence graph appropriately scaled is compared with
the simple percentage age incidence of the first type there
will be little obvious difference from normal communities,
since the numbers of children and adolescents in each of

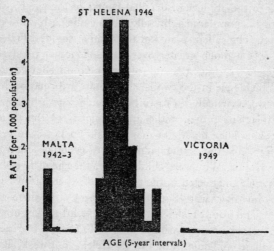

Fig. 3. Age incidence of poliomyelitis in the three
epidemics shown. Each black column corresponds to a
5-year period, 0–5 years, 5–10 years, and so on. See text.

the four first five-year groups – the important ones for
polio – are nearly equal. The height of the peak in any
epidemic will, however, be a measure of the intensity of
attack, and by the second type of age-incidence graph we
can legitimately compare both the intensity of epidemics
and their distribution over the age groups.

In Figure 3 are corrected age-incidence graphs for two epidemics of particular interest. Both were island epidemics involving a small strictly circumscribed area, but the natures of the populations concerned differed greatly. In Malta, 1943, there was a large urban community that had been part of Mediterranean civilization for three thousand years. St Helena, 1947, is a much smaller community inhabiting an island that is one of the proverbially lonely spots of the world. The graphs shown are only approximately corrected owing to the absence of detailed figures of the age constitution of the populations, but allow of a sufficiently valid comparison. The salient points of the comparison are, first, that there was a much greater over-all incidence of paralysis in St Helena; second, that the 0–5-year group showed about equal incidence in the two islands; and third, that on Malta there were virtually no cases in the older age groups which on St Helena provided the great majority of the patients. The experience on Malta may be said to pose the central problem for the understanding and eventual control of poliomyelitis. Why were children over the age of five almost completely unaffected in the presence of what was obviously a very invasive virus? Something was protecting them which was absent from St Helena. We can extend the argument a little further by comparing a normal English, American, or Australian epidemic with the St Helena outbreak. By the same reasoning something is protecting adolescents between ten and twenty in these countries which was not functioning on St Helena.

Any epidemiologist approaching such a problem would immediately offer the opinion that when a disease which can under any conditions affect adults shows a concentration of activity on some younger age group, this is likely to be associated with extensive natural immunization. Whenever we have a common infection which produces a relatively large number of mild or unrecognized attacks for each typical illness and which renders the individual increasingly resistant after each infection, the age-incidence of the manifest disease will show its highest level at the earliest age at which children become exposed to the source of infection. We can be quite definite that poliomyelitis is a disease which falls into this general class.

If immunity is of great importance in determining the

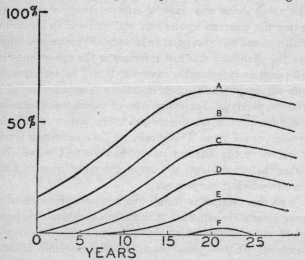

Fig. 4. A family of curves to illustrate the age incidence of paralysis to be expected in a completely non-immune population exposed to poliomyelitis virus of different invasiveness. See text.

pattern of poliomyelitis in a community it would obviously be highly desirable to know, as a background for discussion, what would be the behaviour of poliomyelitis virus in a wholly non-immune group of people. For obvious reasons it is impossible to carry out elaborate investigations on people who have practically no contact with civilized life, and all the evidence we have is in the form of more or less accurate accounts of epidemics of poliomyelitis in such communities. From such accounts, including the St Helena epidemic, and from a variety of other considerations, I have drawn a diagram (Fig. 4) to give my own interpretation of what would happen in non-immune groups exposed to universal infection with polio viruses of different invasiveness. The graph shows what may be called a family of curves, all having the common feature of a highest point in the young adult age and a lowest point in infancy. These curves represent the likelihood that first infection at the age in question will result in recognizable paralysis. It will be seen that for some of the curves infection in infancy is assumed never to produce paralysis. For every type of infectious disease we find differences in the disease-producing power of different 'strains' of the virus. This is why we have to show a family of curves in the diagram rather than a single curve. The higher the general level of a curve, the more invasive is the virus to which it corresponds.

With this diagram in front of us it is possible to visualize more clearly the situation in regard to the Malta epidemic (or of any epidemic which shows a similar age incidence of paralysis). In the years preceding the epidemic of 1943 Malta recorded occasional cases of polio in young children, never more than ten in a year. Suppose we assume that for many years polio virus of type corresponding to line C had been abundant in the community, so abundant that average first contact took place at the age of one or two years and that by the age of five practically all children had had at least two infections and were immune to any invasive action of the virus. Since all first infections took place in children under five years of age, only an extremely small proportion would show any signs of paralysis. Past experience of infection would be so

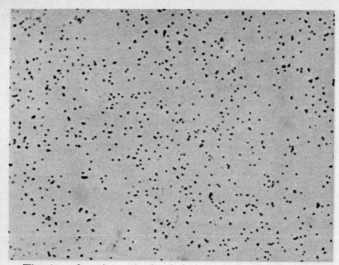

1. The virus of vaccinia stained and photographed with ordinary light. (× 1,000)

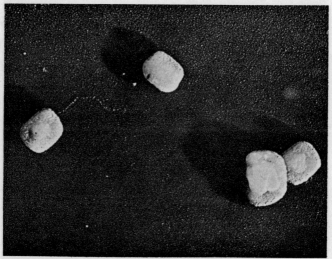

2. The same virus metal-shadowed and photographed in the electron microscope. (× 60,000)

3. The virus of psittacosis, showing the wrinkled appearance after being dried for electron microscopy, metal-shadowed. ($\times$ 12,000)

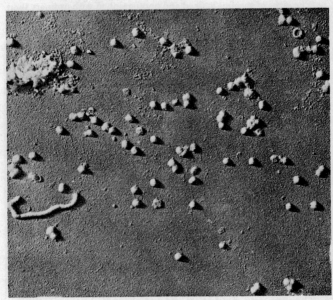

4. Influenza virus particles showing one 'long form' amongst many spherical particles. Electron micrograph metal-shadowed. ($\times$ 6,000)

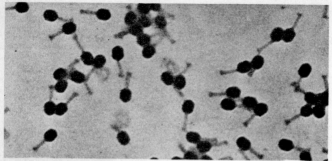

5. A bacterial virus, Bacteriophage T2, photographed directly under the electron microscope. ($\times$ 40,000)

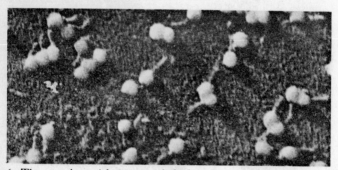

6. The same bacterial virus metal-shadowed.

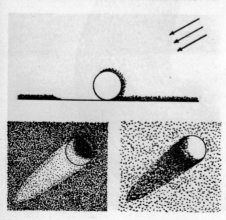

7. A diagram to show the principle of metal-shadowing. A sphere resting on the supporting membrane is bombarded in the direction of the arrows by metal atoms which pile up as shown, producing regions opaque to electrons. The appearance of positive and negative prints when the electron beam passes vertically is shown below.

Nos. 8-11. Influenza virus attached to red cell ghosts.

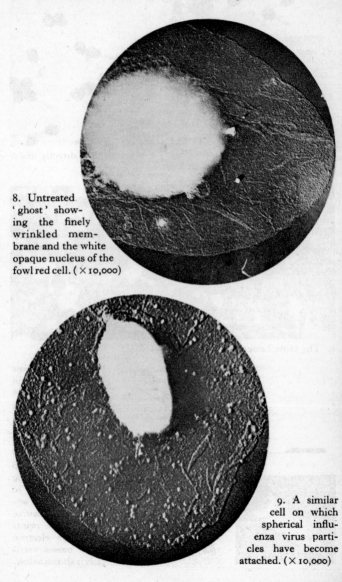

8. Untreated 'ghost' showing the finely wrinkled membrane and the white opaque nucleus of the fowl red cell. (×10,000)

9. A similar cell on which spherical influenza virus particles have become attached. (×10,000)

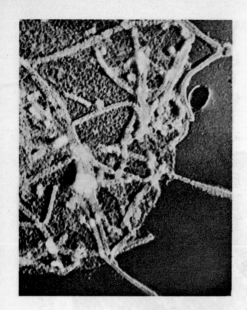

10. Long forms of virus on the red cell surface. (× 25,000)

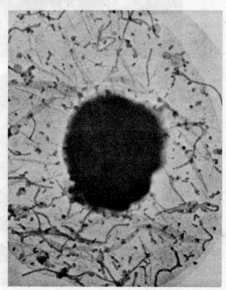

11. A similar preparation photographed directly. (× 12,000)

Virus pocks on the surface of the chorioallantoic membrane of the chick embryo.

Red cell agglutination by influenza virus.

14. The first tube shows the compact button of normal cells settled to the bottom. In the second, clumped cells have produced a ragged deposit, and in the third they have stuck to the glass. Both these tubes contained virus.

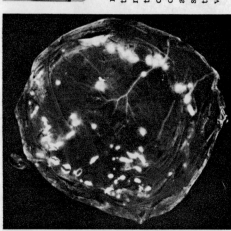

13. Smallpox on the membrane. This egg was inoculated with the blood of a patient at the height of the disease.

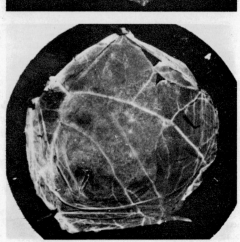

12. Uninfected membrane.

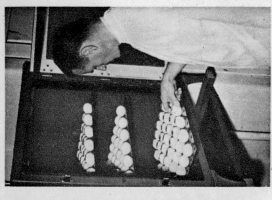

15. Drilling the eggs.

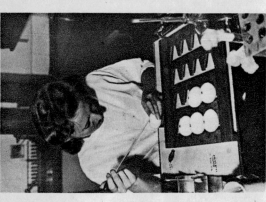

16. Inoculation.

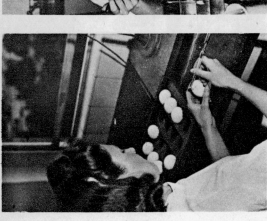

17. Incubation while the virus multiplies.

Egg culture of viruses in the laboratory.

Egg culture of influenza virus on the commercial scale.

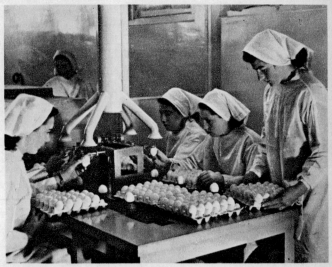

18. Drilling the eggs: note the exhaust hoods to take away irritating shell dust.

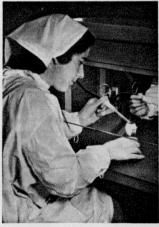

19. Inoculated eggs being incubated.

20. Harvesting the fluids under a glass shield.

universal in children over five that there would be virtually no one susceptible to paralysis in the older age groups.

Now, suppose that there is introduced into such a community the strain corresponding to curve A. The actual extent of spread of the virus may be no more than previously, but with this virus a much higher proportion of the young non-immune children who are infected will show paralysis. Immunization by C-type virus in the past will be an effective protection against the more invasive strain and the result will be just that shown in the actual age incidence of the 1943 epidemic.

For any epidemic of poliomyelitis the observed incidence at different ages can in general be interpreted in accordance with three variable factors:

(1) The invasiveness of the virus concerned.
(2) The ease with which the virus spreads in different age groups with its bearing both on immunization by past virus infection and on the chance of being infected with the current invasive strain of virus.
(3) The influence of isolation in the past on preventing the possibility of immunization.

Admittedly we may find the greatest difficulty in assessing how readily virus moves through the community (2), but we can be fairly certain that it moves most readily when the circumstances which allow the transfer of faecal contamination are most favourable. Poverty, crowding, low standards of personal hygiene, and high environmental temperature are the obvious ones. What must be recognized clearly, as the very centre of the paradox of poliomyelitis, is that conditions favouring the spread of infection if they persist from year to year will favour immunization rather than paralysis. It is on the average much better to meet one's first infection at the age of one or two than at the age of ten and better at ten

D

than at twenty. In any community 'saturated' with the virus, first infection, nearly always at the most favourable age, will produce an insignificantly small annual crop of paralysis. The reading favoured by most epidemiologists is that the appearance of polio epidemics at the end of the nineteenth century did not mean that a newly evolved virus was making its first appearances as a human pathogen, but that only then did conditions begin to arise that interfered with this process of early immunization in communities saturated with the virus.

So far in this discussion we have spoken as if there were only one immunological type of polio virus. The fact that there are three which are to a large extent independent in the sense of immunizing only against their own type, introduces a complication which may become progressively important as time goes on. In the past and in America at least up to the present it seems that all three types moved through the population more or less uniformly. Average human blood, for instance, obtained from American adults contains approximately the same amount of antibody against all three types. This will probably not hold for isolated communities. Already, for instance, it has been shown that a group of Eskimos in Alaska showed antibody against only one of the three types – along with circumstantial evidence that an epidemic of this type had visited the district nineteen to twenty years previously.

If we make the appropriate reservations implied by the existence of three immune types of virus, it is legitimate to discuss the changes that have taken place in the character of poliomyelitis during the last fifty years, as if a single type of virus were concerned.

In the community where the casual attitude towards human excreta of all centuries before the nineteenth persists, and there is early infection of virtually all children with the virus of polio, there will probably be long periods in which paralytic poliomyelitis is never recognized at all. As we have discussed already in regard to Malta, if an unduly virulent strain enters we shall find an epidemic of paralytic disease practically confined to the youngest age group. It should be stressed that immunization of this sort depends not only on poor sanitary habits, but also on the presence of the virus or viruses in the human group concerned. As a general rule, when a virus of any sort is introduced into a small community which has no subsequent contact with the outside world, the resulting epidemic runs its course and the virus disappears within a few weeks or months. It is only when we are dealing with communities in normal human commerce with the rest of the world that we can regard infestation with all the common viruses as a normal continuing condition.

With the development of Western twentieth-century civilization with its emphasis on cleanliness of habits, toilet training, sterilization of feeding utensils, and general improvement in the standard of living, there must inevitably be a postponement in the average age at which infection first occurs. Sooner or later this results in the situation that the standard age of first contact is not in babyhood, but in the early school years. This is still one of the less vulnerable ages, but more so than infancy. When low-grade, i.e. relatively non-invasive virus is about, the vast bulk of these first infections will be unnoticed or give rise to trivial illness without paralysis. But when an actively invasive strain appears we have an epidemic of typical modern type. It will spread rather slowly, and, thanks to the same improving habits in regard to cleanliness, will by no means involve every potentially susceptible individual. There is now general agreement that polio virus spreads principally by close personal association between children – some think that transfer from child to child is mainly by the inhalation of infected droplets of saliva. Others – a majority – feel that one must, if necessary, call a spade a spade and admit the readiness with which infected faeces can be transferred via fingers and mouths to other children. Whatever the mode of spread, a considerable proportion of children will escape infection, a higher proportion in those from comfortable homes than in those from crowded surroundings. If no artificial means of immunization against polio is developed and applied, and if there is a continuing improvement in the standard of living and of personal hygiene through all classes of the community, one might expect the following changes in regard to polio incidence. There will be a further diminution in the number of cases in infancy, and a gradual increase in the total number of cases in the ages from five onwards with a progressive broadening and flattening of the age-incidence graph. More adolescents and adults will be involved, and, as in these age groups the disease is more severe, the over-all mortality of the disease will probably rise. It is inconceivable that the incidence and mortality will ever reach the level that is or has been shown in primitive unhygienic communities where by the accident of isolation no past immunization by the virus has occurred.

Such a pessimistic forecast would, of course, only be valid if no practical method of prevention were developed. Polio research is moving so rapidly at present that in October, 1954, one is not even sure that the proof of the efficacy of vaccination against paralysis has not already been obtained. However, we can be reasonably certain that in one way or another effective means of prevention will be available before the end of the 1950s. These possibilities can now be discussed.

The prevention of poliomyelitis

There have been a number of attempts in the past to develop logical methods of preventing paralytic poliomyelitis. Their nature depended necessarily on what was the current understanding of the epidemiology of the disease and those that were tested in practice had no significant effect. With the development of the modern view of polio epidemiology which has been described, there has been a gradual realization of the directions along which research and administrative action should develop.

The first point to be stressed is that there is no possibility of destroying the virus completely. Even if the physical means of doing so were available, the danger of developing a non-immune population of adults as a result would be extreme as long as there was a possibility that anywhere in the world a focus of infection persisted. If we have to live with the virus the obvious objective is to recapture in essentials the conditions in the early and middle nineteenth century when, despite the ubiquity of the virus, paralytic polio practically did not occur. There can be no question of turning back the clock in regard to cleanliness. The simple medical advantages of effective sanitation and decent habits far outweigh the increase in poliomyelitis. Some acceptable alternative mode of immunization must be found, and the discovery in 1949–50 by Dr J. F. Enders, of Boston, that polio virus would grow well in tissue culture has provided the means of making this a reality.

The standard method for polio virus culture in 1954 is by the use of tissue cultures of monkey kidney. The freshly-removed kidney is cut into large numbers of fragments about a millimetre across and half a dozen of these are fixed to the wall of a glass test tube and provided with a c.c. of suitable fluid to sustain their growth. Hundreds of such tubes can be prepared from a single kidney. They are first incubated for three to four days to allow cells to grow out from the tissue fragments and make a thin sheet on the surface of the glass. Then a small amount of the polio virus is added and incubation continued. The virus invades the cells, multiplies, and the descendant virus soon infects any cells that escaped the first addition of virus. Within four days all cells of the culture are infected and are showing gross evidence of damage under the microscope.

Only a small proportion of them remains alive, and appropriate tests show that very large amounts of new polio virus are present in the fluid and the damaged cells.

A tube of this tissue culture of monkey cells is, from the virologist's point of view, exactly equivalent to a mouse, a chick embryo – or a whole monkey. It provides a means by which polio virus can be grown and by which the fact of its growth can be easily recognized. By suitable modifications of technique the method can be used to isolate the virus from the faeces of cases or contacts, to measure the antibody response after infection and to grow virus in the large amounts needed for the preparation of vaccines. It is not too much to say that the application of tissue culture to polio research has within less than five years completely changed the outlook on the disease.

The availability of potentially unlimited amounts of virus grown in tissue culture made it possible for the first time to think seriously of a killed virus vaccine as immunizing agent. The Salk vaccine is prepared from tissue culture virus by filtration and treatment with formalin followed by rigid tests for safety and immunizing power in monkeys. Large-scale tests of this vaccine were made in the United States during 1954. Much preliminary work in the preceding two years had shown that the vaccine produced remarkably effective antibody response in children, and there is a general expectation amongst virologists that the results of the test will show that at least short-term protection of children against paralysis is possible.

Nevertheless, even before the results of the Salk vaccine tests are available some are advocating the development of living virus vaccines as, in the long run, a safer proposition. There is much activity in the production of new attenuated strains of virus of all three types in the hope that if, for example, by rapid transfer from one tissue culture to another, a given virus loses its power to paralyse monkeys, it will also fail to produce paralytic disease in children. The intention is to find strains of virus which can be given by mouth to children and will induce an immunizing infection of the intestinal tissues without risk of paralysis. This would, of course, represent the closest equivalent to the normal process by which the great majority of children develop immunity against all three viruses before they are adolescent. There are two main difficulties, both aspects of the same dilemma, that if we attenuate the virus too much it will fail to 'take' in many persons and produce no immunity while, if it is still potentially virulent, an occasional unduly susceptible child will be paralysed by the vaccine. With further advance in the understanding of virus variation it may well become possible to separate the virulence needed to ensure a good antibody response from the virulence which allows the virus to attack the nerve cells of the spinal cord. Already there have been reports that considerable numbers of children have been immunized by one type of polio virus given by mouth and that no ill-effects were observed.

In 1952 and 1953 much use was made in the United States of gamma globulin (concentrated antibody) prepared from human blood as short-term protection against paralytic infection. There is good evidence that children injected with the globulin are protected for from four to six weeks but probably not for any longer period. Theoretically, about four injections spread over the warmer months of each year would be needed to provide nearly complete protection. Unfortunately, each dose injected must be prepared by concentrating all the antibody in about a pint of human blood into a few c.c.s of liquid. If sufficient gamma globulin was to be produced to shield all children, every adult in the country would need to provide two or more blood donations each year. In addition, an army of technically trained personnel would be needed to process and administer the material. Such a project is clearly impracticable and probably no one seriously regards the use of gamma globulin as

more than a makeshift. Probably one of the main results of
these tests of passive protection by gamma globulin will be to
assess the possibility that, while the antibody prevents the virus
from producing paralysis, it does not prevent its immunizing
the patient. In this way both short-term and long-lasting immunity could be produced. I should still expect that when the
various methods have been tested in practice over a sufficient
number of years, the final choice will prove to be the adminis-
tration of living virus vaccines by mouth under the protection
of an appropriate dose of gamma globulin.

Whatever the result of current work on immunization, it will
probably be several years before we have universal, safe, and
effective immunization against polio. In the meantime is there
anything useful that we can do to minimize its effects? There
is not much that can be recommended with any enthusiasm.
To a large extent, the automatic reactions of ordinary people
offer as sound a basis as any. If in a given summer only an occasional case is being reported, children should be allowed their
normal activities in the hope that they will be infected and
immunized by the prevalent non-invasive virus. When an 'epidemic' is recognized, i.e. when a more than usually invasive
strain is about, an effort should be made to avoid infection.
Children should not mix in play with more than limited groups
of others, at school there should be indoctrination in methods
of avoiding faecal contamination, swimming pools should be
closed. There is scope for research into substances otherwise
harmless which will kill polio virus with certainty – most ordinary antiseptics are almost inert against it. Some have suggested that there are organic mercurial compounds which, given
to a child with polio, will prevent excretion of the virus. Such
might also be used for children who were only potential carriers.
At a less ambitious level there is the provision of a foolproof and
practicable technique for eliminating the possibility of virus re-
maining on children's hands after any visit to the lavatory.

These ideas are concerned with preventing infection by an invasive epidemic type of polio virus. There is a second line of action – to endeavour to prevent paralysis following infection. Here advice must be mainly negative. There are some things that are known to increase the likelihood that an infection by the virus will take paralytic form. Children who have their tonsils surgically removed during an epidemic are significantly more likely than others to suffer from the dangerous bulbar poliomyelitis that affects the centres in the brain for breathing and swallowing. In both Australia and England it has been found that children might develop severe paralysis if they were immunized against whooping cough and diphtheria at a time when they were exposed to poliomyelitis. It is probably safe to immunize babies under nine months but, in the light of present knowledge, it is safer to defer immunization of older infants and children until the epidemic is past. Over-exertion at the times when invasion by the virus is taking place tends to increase paralysis in the muscles involved. During the currency of an epidemic parents should insist that any child a little off-colour should go to bed for a day or two, and they should be adamant that a boy or girl with any headache or feeling of not being quite fit should not engage in competitive sport.

There is no drug available which has any effect on the virus in the nervous system, nor is there any serious hope that present experimental work will lead to the discovery of one. Treatment is directed wholly towards counteracting the physical results of paralysis and training the unparalysed muscles to take over as much as possible of the work of the paralysed ones.

CHAPTER EIGHT

INFLUENZA

SOMETIME in most winters and not infrequently at other seasons large numbers of people suffer from a sharp short-lasting fever associated with signs of infection in the air passages. Every few years such epidemics are much more widespread, involving 10 or 20 per cent of the population, and once only in the history of epidemics what seemed to be an enormously more virulent prevalence of the same type swept over the world – in 1918–19. All these conditions are popularly called influenza. It is still impossible to give a name that means anything to many of these acute respiratory infections, but we can say that all the extensive epidemics of what is called typical influenza that have occurred since 1933 have been due to one or other of two well-defined viruses known amongst virologists as influenza viruses A and B. The nature of the great pandemic of 1918–19 has never been established, but most authorities would probably agree – at least there is nothing to disprove the hypothesis – that it was due primarily to influenza viruses resembling the modern A types.

In the earlier chapters of this book influenza viruses have been very largely used for the discussion and exemplification of many of the general properties of viruses. Once the viruses have been isolated their ability to grow readily in the chick embryo and to agglutinate red blood cells make them particularly easy to handle, and a great deal is known about their properties. This same ease of handling has also stimulated the study of influenza as it occurs in man and of the experimental disease produced by infecting animals with the virus.

The first isolation of a virus from human influenza was made in 1933 by an English team of research workers headed by the late Sir Patrick Laidlaw. Two years previously, however, a virus now known to be very closely related to influenza virus A was isolated from pigs with the disease known in America as swine influenza or 'hog flu'.

The events leading to the isolation of human influenza virus are worth mentioning. Ever since the great influenza epidemic of 1890 bacteriologists had been interested in discovering the organism responsible for the disease. In 1893 Pfeiffer, a German bacteriologist, had claimed that a bacterium now called *Haemophilus influenzae* was the cause. Extensive investigations of the 1918–19 epidemic showed that no special types of bacteria were consistently present, and there was a considerable body of opinion in favour of the view that the primary agent must have been a virus. No one succeeded, however, in demonstrating that a virus was present, even with the use in some cases of human volunteers. By the end of 1932 techniques for virus study were much more advanced than in 1919, and in particular Laidlaw and Dunkin had just completed a successful study of the virus disease dog distemper which many people regarded as essentially similar to human influenza. When a fairly severe influenza epidemic hit London in December, 1932, Laidlaw, Andrewes, and Wilson Smith undertook primarily to see whether, by injection of material from the throats of patients with influenza, anything resembling influenza could be produced in experimental animals. They were prepared to try all available animals, from white mice to horses, but in fact almost the first animals they tried gave them their answer. During the work on distemper Laidlaw had found that in addition to dogs, ferrets were highly susceptible, usually dying of the experimental disease. They had proved convenient experimental animals, and methods for handling ferrets so as to prevent any accidental unwanted infections had been worked out. The whole experimental set-up for this work was still available, so it was natural to test the susceptibility of ferrets to the material that they hoped contained the virus of influenza.

I can vividly remember the excitement that went around the National Institute of Medical Research at Hampstead when the ferrets developed symptoms unmistakably similar to human influenza. Two days after a throat washing from a human patient had been dropped into their noses they developed a high fever, lost their appetites, and curled up miserably. Their noses began to run and they even sneezed! It was a relatively mild disease, and, as in human beings, the fever abated in four or five days and the animals recovered completely. There was hardly any doubt right from the beginning that it really was influenza that had been given to the ferrets, and all subsequent work has supported this conclusion. It was found, for instance, that when a patient had recovered from influenza his blood serum contained antibody that would, when mixed with virus, render it incapable of producing influenza on inoculation into a ferret.

Ferrets, however, are not the most convenient of laboratory animals; they are expensive, difficult to breed, and they bite. The next step in influenza virus research was to show that mice could also be infected, although not with virus straight from the human patient. If the virus had gone through a few 'passages' in ferrets, i.e. transferring nasal material from an infected ferret to a new one in sequence, it could then infect mice, and after a few passages through *them* gave rise to a fatal pneumonia. The degree to which the lungs became solid, airless, and deep plum colour could be used as a measure of the amount of virus that had been inoculated. In the years 1935-40 most experimental work on influenza viruses was carried out on mice and many important results were obtained. In the two years 1940-1 there was a rather dramatic change in the experimental approach. In 1940 I showed that influenza virus would grow freely and produce visible changes in the chick embryo if it were inoculated into the amniotic cavity. This method of inoculation could be used to isolate influenza virus directly from human throat washings, and soon became the standard method of isolation. Following on this several people showed in 1941 that the much simpler method of inoculation into the more superficial allantoic cavity was equally effective for influenza virus once it had been successfully isolated. The method was, however, of no use for isolating the virus from human patients. In the same year Dr George Hirst of the Rockefeller Foundation laboratories made the all-important discovery that fluids from chick embryos infected with influenza virus would clump the red blood cells of chickens or men. Since then most work on problems of influenza virus has been done by a combination of chick embryo culture and haemagglutination. In earlier chapters I have told how this type of work has thrown a great deal of light on the nature of virus action on the cell. It has been equally productive in regard to the problems of influenza as a human disease.

The first essential to the understanding of any infectious disease is to be able to recognize it. This is often by no means easy. For very many years the two diseases typhoid fever and typhus fever were indistinguishable by physicians, although we would now regard them as utterly different in almost every essential. It was not long before it was found that not all infectious fevers labelled influenza by doctor and patient were due to the virus that had infected the ferrets in 1933. Out of the hotch-potch of acute respiratory infections it became necessary to sort out those which on the basis of laboratory tests were 'true influenza', i.e. infections due to the newly isolated virus. By 1937 it was possible to say that influenza virus characteristically produced the sort of influenza that occurs in acute widespread epidemics. When only occasional cases were occurring during a winter these gave no evidence of being due to influenza virus. However, even this generalization did not always hold. There was for instance a typical large epidemic in America in 1936, which was not due to the virus that Laidlaw and his colleagues had isolated. Then from a similar American epidemic in 1940 Dr Thomas Francis isolated another sort of virus obviously resembling the first but with no immunological relationship to it. This virus is now known as influenza B, in contrast to the influenza A virus isolated in 1933. A third type of influenza virus was found in 1948 and is known as influenza C. It is apparently widespread in most countries but produces only the most trivial of symtoms. It is certainly of no great importance in comparison with influenza A and B, and will not be mentioned again.

In investigating any outbreak with the general character of influenza the first practical job is to find whether it is due to A or B virus, or to neither. This is now a fully standardized procedure. First one locates a few patients in the first acute stage of the disease with a temperature of at least 100° F. These are given an ounce of salt solution to gargle; this is then returned to a test-tube, where it is mixed with a solution 'serum-broth' that helps to preserve the virus. At the same time a sample of blood is taken from the patient's veins. This is allowed to clot and the fluid serum separated, labelled 'Serum I', and placed in the refrigerator. A fortnight later the same patient is bled again to provide 'Serum II'. These three fluids are the raw materials for the laboratory tests.

The throat washings are filtered through sterilized ordinary filter paper to get rid of particles of food, etc., and then penicillin and streptomycin are added to prevent the growth of bacteria. A few drops are then inoculated into the amniotic cavity of each of six chick embryos that have been incubated for thirteen days. The eggs are sealed and put back into an incubator for five days. The amniotic fluid and the lungs are then removed from each embryo and tested for their ability to agglutinate human or guinea-pig red cells. If influenza virus is present the cells will show typical clumping. After this it is usual to 'adapt' the virus to growth in the allantoic cavity before testing whether it is of A or B type. This is very simple in theory, although in practice there are some complications. If it is type A, a known anti-A serum will inactivate it so that it will not agglutinate red cells; an anti-B serum will have no such action.

It is a much simpler matter to determine from the two samples of serum whether the patient has had true influenza and whether it was type A or B. Tests are made to see how active each sample is in inactivating given amounts of standard A and B viruses. We can express that activity in numerical fashion as so many units of antibody, and we may tabulate the kind of result one would expect from a case of influenza A as follows:

	Antibody against	
	Influenza A	*Influenza B*
Serum I	10	20
Serum II	500	20

There is a rise in antibody between first and second bleeds of the type corresponding to the virus involved. In most laboratories a second kind of test, a complement fixation reaction that depends on a somewhat different principle, is also used to differentiate A and B infections. It has definite advantages over the simple neutralization test, but the theory of the reaction is too complicated to be discussed here.

In dealing with an actual epidemic it is usual to be content with isolating a small number of samples of virus, but to obtain first and second samples of serum from large numbers of typical cases, doubtful cases, and people who have been exposed but have shown no symptoms. When these are worked out we know pretty accurately the nature and extent of the epidemic.

We can now say something about the behaviour of influenza A and B in Europe, America, and Australia since 1933. On the basis of studies in various laboratories we can present a diagram like Figure 5 which shows the main epidemics. It

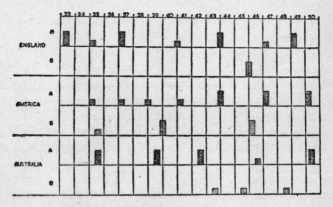

Fig. 5. The history of influenza epidemics since the discovery of the virus in 1933. The blocks represent epidemics in which virus was isolated in the three countries shown. The bigger blocks indicate extensive epidemics.

will be seen that epidemics are always at least two years apart, influenza A tending to be at two- or three-year intervals, while major influenza B epidemics are usually four to six years apart. In recent years many isolations of A and B virus have been made in intermediate years or from small outbreaks unassociated with a typical widespread epidemic. Influenza A has consistently tended to be more frequent and more important than B. Much more work has been done with A, and general concepts of how influenza epidemics arise and spread have been developed mainly around influenza A. Also there is a little circumstantial evidence that the great influenza epidemic of 1918–19 was due to influenza A viruses.

If for the time being we omit influenza before 1933 and concentrate on influenza A the picture that emerges is something like this.

Influenza A virus is wholly a human parasite in the sense that infection is always derived fairly directly from another infected human being. Epidemics occur only when *seasonal conditions are appropriate*, almost wholly in winter and spring, and when there is *a large enough population of individuals non-immune* to the particular virus active at the time. In between epidemic periods the virus survives as trickling streams of infection in non-immune individuals, often without actual symptoms being produced. When a typical big influenza epidemic has passed through a country most non-immunes have probably been infected either with fever or without symptoms and have become immune. This immunity gradually fades, but it is probable that if the virus remained constant in character the great majority of people would retain an effective immunity for at least five or six years. It is gradually becoming certain, however, that the virus does not remain constant. Influenza virus is a highly labile organism prone to mutation of many types including mutation in immunological character. Such inheritable changes in character have never been so great as to render an A virus unrecognizable as A or convert it to B, but they have been sufficient to allow an animal immune to one type to be susceptible to the changed form. It appears that to survive as an agent of human disease influenza A virus needs to be undergoing a more or less steady sequence of changes in its immunological character. The form that immunized a city population two years previously cannot provoke an epidemic there, but if one of its descendants has changed by mutation so that antibody against the old form is no longer effective, this descendant virus *can* initiate an epidemic. The facts are that each new epidemic of influenza A seems to be due to virus differing to a greater or lesser extent from all previous viruses in these immunological characters. It is only an assumption, but a very likely assumption, that the mutability of influenza virus is an essential requirement for its surivival as a species.

The great pandemic of 1918–19

Within the last century there have been two epidemics of influenza intense enough and extending widely enough to merit the term pandemics, epidemics involving the whole of the world's population. These occurred in 1890–2 and in 1918–19. The latter was by far the more devastating of the two. In England the epidemic of 1890 broke on a population which for some reason had not experienced a definite influenza epidemic since 1857. There were extremely large numbers of cases in the three waves of the epidemic and many deaths, especially in older people. Naturally nothing is known about the virus responsible, but one's impression is strong that the epidemic was quite similar to a modern influenza A epidemic. Its extent was probably due simply to the fact that for some unknown reason there had been an unusually long gap since the last epidemic of influenza A.

From 1890 onward there were recurrent epidemics of influenza in England which appear to have been quite similar in character to the epidemics of influenza A and B which have been verified since 1933. In 1918, however, something unprecedented occurred. In England an acute epidemic of influenza broke out in the second week of June – it had clearly been brought from France by soldiers on leave from the Western Front. In that week there was a sudden change in the age incidence of deaths ascribed to influenza. Instead of deaths being concentrated in the oldest age groups plus some in infancy, they involved *young adults*. This epidemic in early summer spread widely through the community and, considering the very large number of people who were infected, the death rate was quite low. The disturbing feature, however, was the sinister concentration of mortality on the young adult. This was to be characteristic of the pandemic throughout its course, both in its early mild phase and its subsequent killing waves. The summer epidemic died down, but in August a new wave of cases began with a frighteningly high mortality. This wave in England reached its acme in October. Another lull was followed by a winter wave also of high mortality. Influenza remained unduly active and unduly fatal through 1919 and 1920, but gradually reverted to normal character. The change from the young adult incidence of fatality to the standard type involving virtually only the old was not complete until 1929. The pandemic involved the whole world and the total death roll probably exceeded 25,000,000 persons. The greatest absolute mortality was in India, where it was sufficient to wipe out the whole population increase over the decade 1911–21. In some small communities where the whole population was stricken almost simultaneously nearly 50 per cent died. In most countries with accurate vital statistics and populations predominantly of European origin the mortality rate was about 5 per 1,000 of the population. In countries like South Africa and New Zealand the non-European death rate was four to ten times higher than that of whites in the same country. Only a few very isolated places escaped the pandemic completely. The largest was New Caledonia, and the list also included New Guinea and some other islands in the South-west Pacific and St Helena.

It is not possible to give an accurate account of the origin and spread of the epidemic. In 1940 Miss Clark and I published a monograph in which this was discussed in detail, and here we can only present a brief statement of the conclusions we reached in that monograph. Influenza of the new type first appeared around April, 1918, in Western France, in the region where large numbers of American troops were being poured into Europe. There had been moderately intense epidemics of 'ordinary' influenza in both America and Europe in the immediately preceding winter and spring, and there is therefore a strong suggestion that in some way the mingling of large numbers of Americans and Europeans, with their associated viruses, was responsible for the genesis of the new type of influenza. From France the epidemic passed to Spain, where it first created real public alarm, and received the name Spanish influenza by which, in English-speaking countries, it was generally referred to at the time. The summer epidemic spread over most of Europe, and other similar and presumably related epidemics are referred to from places as far apart as West Africa and Chungking in the heart of China. The change from the mild summer wave to the much more lethal autumn type took place close to the Western Front, where the great battles of July and August, 1918, were being fought. It spread rapidly to every major part of the globe. There are hints that the change to the lethal type took place independently at more than one point, but it seems more reasonable to assume that the change occurred in France and spread thence at the speed and in the direction of human movement.

Pandemic influenza entered America at Boston on August 12 and flared across the continent within a month. It reached Australia and New Zealand in October. In New Zealand it spread through the country at once, but in Australia stringent quarantine regulations – or perhaps some other factor unknown – prevented any outbreak until February, 1919. The peak of the Australian epidemic was in August, 1919, and it was only in that month that pandemic influenza reached Tasmania. This was the last sizeable community to be reached anywhere in the world, and it is probably significant that the mortality that resulted was the lowest of any state in Australia and for that matter of any major community in the world.

There is some evidence that human beings were not the only victims. In South Africa large numbers of baboons died at the time, and it may be that the popular ascription of their deaths to influenza was correct. A much more substantial story concerns the swine influenza of Iowa and other Mid-Western American states. Dr Richard Shope, the outstanding authority on that disease, says that there is unanimity amongst farmers and veterinarians that 'hog flu' was unknown before 1918 and was actually first seen at the Iowa State Fair which, in 1918, coincided with the time of the first experience of pandemic influenza in that state. The disease has persisted since, breaking out in the late autumn each year. In 1931 Shope and Lewis found that hog flu was a complex infection due to the association of a virus and a bacterium. A few years later it was shown that the virus was closely related to human influenza A virus. Others showed that in association with a human epidemic in 1937 pigs fed on garbage developed evidence of infection with virus of the current human type. Most virologists would probably agree that the weight of evidence supports Shope's contention that the swine virus is a lineal descendant of the virus or one of the viruses of pandemic influenza. There are, however, many who, like myself, would regard our current influenza A viruses as also having had the pandemic viruses in their 'ancestral tree'. We can be certain of nothing in this field apart from the fact that influenza viruses are extremely variable and it is in no way inconceivable that descendants of the same virus after thirty years' passage through different hosts should differ greatly in many important characteristics. Swine influenza virus is of importance in relation to pandemic influenza only if there is reason to believe that it has been maintained in the pig cycle with less change in its immunological type than would have occurred if it had survived by the normal course of passage from one human being to another over the same period of years.

The pandemic of 1918-19, as I have said, was an unprecedented occurrence – a type of epidemic which we can be quite certain had never previously involved any community whose historical records have survived. We do not know what were the initiating circumstances. Immediately after the pandemic it was natural to conclude that the situation created in Europe by the first World War had been responsible in some way. It was not difficult to 'think up' a plausible story along such lines, but if war circumstances in 1918 were responsible we should surely have seen a similar pandemic some time between 1940 and 1946. In 1944-6 Europe suffered far greater social disorganization than in 1918, and there were other factors such as crowding into air-raid shelters that would have been expected to favour respiratory disease. But there was no influenza to speak of until the first months of 1949. We are left with the unsatisfying hypothesis that the pandemic was due simply to some accident of mutation or recombination that gave rise to a virus of unusual invasiveness and capacity to spread. Once this step was taken the subsequent development of enormous amounts of virus would automatically provide opportunities for further mutations to occur. It has recently been suggested that one series of mutations to greater virulence may have taken place in the fighting zone itself as a result of exposure of the virus to mustard gas. Compounds of mustard gas type, in particular the so-called nitrogen-mustard, are known to increase the mutation rate of a variety of organisms, and the suggestion is a logical one.

Finally, we must not forget that the evidence suggests that a great many, perhaps most, of the deaths were due not to virus infection as such, but to the activity of various bacteria which found a soil in which they could flourish in the lungs damaged by the virus.

The prevention of influenza

In discussing the prevention of influenza the first question to be put is whether it is worth attempting to do so. Now, there is no question that influenza, even in the absence of a pandemic, is a killing disease. Whenever an influenza A epidemic appears there is a sharp temporary increase in deaths, most of which, however, are not ascribed to influenza. Deaths of old people ill for some other reason are characteristically increased by influenza. The severe epidemic of influenza in England during January, 1951, showed this clearly. In Liverpool, which was very heavily hit, the number of deaths in the worst week of the epidemic exceeded that of the worst week in the 1918–19 pandemic. In 1951, however, deaths were almost wholly amongst older people. There were few in persons under fifty-five but above that age the mortality increased progressively in each five-year age group. A nineteenth-century writer pointed out that one could always deduce the presence of an influenza epidemic when the obituary columns of *The Times* became unusually crowded with deaths of the elderly and the distinguished. The death rate from tuberculosis also shows minor ups and downs which indicate that many persons who would normally die from tuberculosis in one year will die in the previous year if that is marked by a definite epidemic of influenza. The harmless week's illness of a healthy individual is hardly worth preventing except when service men are involved. The prevention of pandemic influenza would, of course, become the greatest of all public health problems should anything of 1918 type arise in the future. As we have indicated, there is no clue whatever as to how the initiation of such a pandemic could be prevented.

Work on the prevention of influenza to date has been concentrated on an attempt to find a method of immunization that would be effective in preventing a disabling incidence of influenza in service men. Within limits these efforts have been successful. A vaccine can be produced from influenza virus grown in chick embryos, concentrated and killed by formalin. A single injection of this will protect about 80 per cent of those who would otherwise have influenza *provided the epidemic in question is due to virus of the same immunological type as is used for production of the vaccine*. With such vaccines effective protection was provided against the influenza A epidemic of November, 1943, and the influenza B epidemic of spring, 1946. The same type of vaccine, however, was wholly ineffective against the American influenza A epidemic of 1947. The reason for this failure was simply that the 1947 epidemic was caused by a type of virus very different immunologically from the virus strains previously current.

This is the whole crux of the problem of immunization against influenza. As we have seen earlier, there is a progressive change in immunological type from epidemic to epidemic. Sometimes the change appears to be more rapid than at other times. This demands that if influenza vaccines are to have any hope of being effective they must be right up to date. When, for instance, there is a sharp epidemic in the Southern Hemisphere one winter, the virus concerned should be added to the vaccine to be used against influenza in the Northern Hemisphere six months later. This, however, is not an easy requirement to fulfil at the practical level. A biological supply firm with an order for, say, five million doses of influenza vaccine to fulfil has to 'tool up' for the work in a way almost analogous to a motor-car factory when it makes a change of the model. In particular it must have the viruses which are to be incorporated in the vaccine, fully adapted to grow freely in chick embryos. This is often exasperatingly difficult to attain, and a new virus may also require some modification of the large-scale techniques previously used. This all takes time and may be very expensive. In practice the maintenance of effective large-scale immunization against influenza is possible only if it is very heavily subsidized from defence funds. It can never become a straightforward standard procedure like immunization against diphtheria.

It is an interesting experience to see the functioning of a large commercial unit producing influenza vaccine. One unit that was in action in Australia during 1945 used approximately 11,000 eggs a day. These arrived at the plant from the poultry farms in the form of embryos at the eleventh day of development. The first step was to verify by a rapid 'candling' process that the embryo had developed to the normal extent and was alive. Then the trays of eggs passed to girls who drilled a small hole in the blunt end of each egg and placed them blunt end upwards in rubber cups on a continuously moving belt. This led them first under a sterilizing ultraviolet lamp and then to the inoculators. These girls had a mechanical syringe fed from a reservoir of dilute 'seed virus', i.e. a 1:10,000 solution of virus-containing fluid from previously infected eggs. One sharp jab and each egg received a tenth of a c.c. of fluid into the allantoic cavity. The next set of operators sealed the hole with a drop of sterile melted wax and transferred the eggs to incubator trays. The trays then went into a giant incubator, where they stayed forty-eight hours while the virus multiplied.

'Harvesting' of the virus was done with sterile precautions under a glass hood. Each egg was placed in a brass eggcup so arranged that it could rotate freely on a vertical axis. To remove the cap of shell at the blunt end where the air space is, the egg was spun around gently against the tip of a very fine oxy-acetylene flame set at the proper level. In this way the cap of the egg could be neatly cut off and the cut edge automatically sterilized by the heat of the flame. The operator then flipped off the top and with sterile scissors opened into the allantoic cavity, cutting the blood-vessels and allowing the embryo blood to mix with the virus-containing fluid. The next girl in the sequence sucked out this bloodstained fluid with a specially guarded tube in which a low negative pressure was maintained, into a receptacle chilled to near freezing point. Here the red cells settled, carrying down with them practically all the virus. The next step was to spin down the red cells in a refrigerated centrifuge and discard the fluid. The cells were then suspended in one-tenth the original volume of salt solution and held at body temperature until all the virus was re-liberated into the solution. This tenfold concentrate was separated, checked for sterility, titrated for its virus content, and finally treated with formalin to give the vaccine.

Suppose that somewhere in the world a highly virulent form of influenza should arise with a concentration of mortality on young adults and an imminent threat of a new pandemic of 1918 type. What in the light of present knowledge could be done to minimize its effects? Attempts to block the spread by quarantine measure would undoubtedly be made, but would probably not be successful in doing more than to slow down the movement of the epidemic at certain points. Virologists and bacteriologists would, of course, provide as rapidly as possible information as to the type of virus concerned and the important associated bacteria. As the pandemic developed a constant watch for mutational changes in the virus would be necessary. Vaccines of the pandemic strain would be produced with the greatest possible speed, but I think we would need to be lucky to have large-scale production sufficiently under way to have a chance of making use of it in areas not yet reached by the pandemic. If, as is likely, new types arose during the course of the epidemics the vaccines would need to be modified accordingly.

There have been two great therapeutic advances made since 1918 which may change the whole aspect of a new pandemic. Death seemed to be largely due to bacterial infection in 1918–19, and there is at least a strong presumption that those deaths could have been prevented by the drugs now available. Penicillin could be expected to deal with pneumococcal, staphylococcal, and streptococcal infections, streptomycin and aureomycin with the Haemophilus influenza (Pfeifer's influenza bacillus), which was very common in 1918–19 and which is insusceptible to penicillin. There is in the minds of many bacteriologists a suspicion that the 1918 virus was in itself the major cause of death and that the bacteria found had only a minor part in determining the issue. If this is so the antibiotics might have proved completely disappointing.

There is another reason for doubting how effective the antibiotic drugs would be if a 1918 type pandemic appeared in the next year or two – the existence of bacteria that are resistant to the drugs. It is notorious how rapidly the staphylococcus (the cause of many boils and other skin infections) becomes resistant to penicillin and the other commonly-used antibiotics. There are nearly always staphylococci in the nose, and it would be amusing if it were not sinister to see how uniformly hospital bacteriologists all round the world have found that a few months after any new antibiotic comes into general use in their hospital the 'staphs' in the noses of the nursing staff begin to show an increasing proportion of resistant types. From our present point of view this is particularly sinister because since 1933 most of the acute deaths from influenza in younger people have been due to a superadded staphylococcal pneumonia. Most pathologists believe the effect of the pandemic virus was to make the air passages vulnerable to any bacteria that might find access. It seems quite likely, therefore, that if a pandemic arose nowadays the free use of antibiotics would almost certainly result in the appearance of resistant and, therefore, dangerous staphylococci as the chief agent of secondary pneumonia.

The other approach to treatment which is of great theoretical interest at the present time is related to the fact we have stressed repeatedly, that the main incidence of death in 1918 was on the young adult. There are more than hints that the work now in progress on pituitary and adrenal hormones (ACTH and cortisone) will throw light on this phenomenon. From what we already know of the therapeutic action of ACTH (adreno-cortico-trophic hormone), I should feel very confident that in a good hospital the combined use of ACTH and the appropriate antibiotics according to the best modern standards would have allowed the recovery of many of the young adults who died in 1918.

In view of the fact that supplies of these potent drugs and of physicians who can use them adequately are bound to be insufficient when patients are numbered in hundreds of millions, we could never hope to save more than a small proportion, but we at least should feel far less impotent than the last generation of physicians did in 1918.

CHAPTER NINE

THE COMMON COLD

LIKE every virologist, I am tired of that inevitable parting shot, 'Yes, but what have you done about the common cold?' No journalist appears to be capable of hearing of any discovery in the virus field without writing that the common cold, a virus disease, causes the loss of x million man-hours of labour and y million pounds' worth of production, and that it is hoped that all these losses may be avoided as a result of the new discovery. All this tends to 'get under our skin', but perhaps after all we should be called upon to explain this failure which is so obvious to everyone else. What have been the results of laboratory investigation of the common cold, and why have they led to no development that can even promise some hope of preventing or curing colds?

Any medical officer of health concerned with infectious disease problems knows that it is often impossible to diagnose the nature of a person's disease without finding out in the laboratory the type of germ responsible. Smallpox and chicken-pox may be very difficult to distinguish without laboratory tests, but administrative action will be widely different depending on which diagnosis is adopted. A cold in the ordinary sense is merely a name for any inflammation of the lining of the nose which causes obstruction to the airways and an increased use of the handkerchief. Some such 'colds' are not infectious at all, but are due to abnormal allergic reaction to chemical substances suspended in the air. Hay fever, in which grass pollen carries the offending chemical, is the commonest. There are, of course, truly infectious colds, episodes which inflict most people about twice a year and spread clearly from person to person within the household, and it is only with these that we are concerned.

The typical cold usually appears to start in the nose with an itchy, stuffy feeling, some sneezing, and then a phase of watery discharge. The following day the discharge becomes mucous and for a variable time there is elimination of mucus, often opaque with the pus cells that signify bacterial infection. The straightforward cold clears up in a week or a fortnight, but in many instances the secondary bacterial phase persists and involves the sinuses of the nose or spreads down into the bronchial tubes. There are many variations in the picture. Some people's colds seem to start primarily in the larynx and involve the nose only a day or two later. Most adults do not show a rise of temperature with an ordinary cold, but children do so more frequently. Here we come up against the real difficulty of being certain of diagnosing any disease of which we cannot define the cause. If we follow a few hundred people through an average winter we shall find most of them having at least one respiratory infection with nasal discharge and some coughing. These will vary greatly in almost every other characteristic, and particularly in the degree of fever and the intensity of the general symptoms of any febrile illness. At one end of the scale we will have a typical mild cold, at another extreme a typical attack of influenza with the fever symptoms coming on abruptly and preceding any signs showing that the infection is a respiratory one. In between there will be found an almost continuous series that will defy any attempt to separate them into two, three, or more distinct diseases. Only if we could isolate and identify the organism responsible would we be in a position to make a rational division of the hotch-potch of conditions that army medical officers called URTI (upper respiratory tract infection) or CURD (common undifferentiated respiratory disease) during World War II.

The proper approach to the problem would be to 'isolate' the agents responsible from a considerable range of such infections, compare them with one another and then develop means of checking the nature of any respiratory infection in the light of differences betweeen the organisms isolated. This sort of approach has worked very well in sorting out cases of bacterial food poisoning, dysentery, and so on, but despite a great deal of effort it has failed completely, or almost completely, in the respiratory virus infections. The true influenzas we can recognize readily enough by the methods described in the last chapter, but when we take these away we still have more than 90 per cent of the infections left. All attempts to prove that these are due to this or that type of bacterium have failed, nor has anyone succeeded in producing a recognizable cold in any animal more accessible than the chimpanzee. Many attempts to grow viruses from colds and the like in chick embryos have either been fruitless or have given results that other virologists have been unable to repeat.

Under the circumstances there is only one experimental approach to the problem available, the use of the human volunteer. It *is* possible to transfer these infections deliberately from one human being to another, but this cannot be regarded as isolating the virus. To work with human volunteers needs a great deal of organization and the expenditure of large sums of money. It would obviously never be a practical proposition to diagnose one man's disease by seeing what happened when it was transferred to eight other men. In the present state of knowledge, however, it is fair to state that if a respiratory infection is not influenza, *that* is the only way in which any sort of exact diagnosis can be made.

According to the American Commission on Respiratory Diseases, which experimented extensively on conscientious objector volunteers during the war, there are three common infections due to viruses other than influenza. They are differentiated primarily by their incubation periods, that is the time elapsing between inoculation, usually by spraying into the nose and throat, and the appearance of symptoms. The typical common cold has an incubation period of one to two days, there is a common feverish infection with a period of around five days, and there is a third disease which often produces no more than a 'cold', but in its full-blown form is labelled atypical virus pneumonia. This has an incubation period of seven to fourteen days. The second short-lasting fever with an incubation period of a few days was and is common in military establishments, but is less frequent or less frequently recognized in civilian life. The most important recent advance in the field of respiratory infections has been the isolation, by two American groups, of viruses which seem to be responsible for human infections of this type. These were described at the end of 1953 simply as cytopathogenic viruses which will grow in tissue cultures of a variety of human cells and produce cell-damaging (cytopathogenic) effects appearing more slowly but otherwise of the same general character as those produced by polio viruses. As yet, nothing has been reported about the natural history of this virus. Even less is known about the third group of fevers, but a little should be said about atypical pneumonia or, as it is more commonly but rather unjustifiably called nowadays, virus pneumonia, before going on to say what has been learnt about human colds.

Atypical pneumonia in its severe form emerged very largely as a by-product of the success of the sulpha-drugs and penicillin in curing pneumonia, due to infection with the pneumococcus. Penicillin in particular is so effective that failure to cure the disease within two days will always throw some doubt on the diagnosis. Gradually it emerged that most pneumonias that failed to respond to penicillin had a special character of their own and that they merged into a series of minor infections not usually requiring hospital treatment. This group received the name of atypical pneumonia. Several research groups have claimed that a virus can be transmitted from these cases to animals, but others have failed and no claim is yet generally accepted. The only useful laboratory advance in the diagnosis of atypical pneumonia is the development of a blood test – 'cold agglutination' whose rationale no one understands, but which is nearly always positive in severe cases of this disease and negative in most other conditions. In the last two years it has been found that the new antibiotic aureomycin has a beneficial effect on atypical pneumonia – a result strongly suggesting that the virus responsible resembles a rickettsia or one of the psittacosis group more than an influenza virus.

The most wholehearted attack on the common cold was started in 1946 by a group of scientists led by Dr C. H. Andrewes and sponsored by the Medical Research Council of Great Britain. Their object was simply to undertake the same sort of experiments with the common cold on human volunteers that thirteen years earlier had been done with influenza on ferrets and had led to the first isolation of the influenza virus. Theoretically the human being should be just as useful as any other experimental animal for the study of any disease to which he is susceptible and which has no serious effect on his general health. But one must, of course, provide rather more elaborate accommodation than served for ferrets and guinea-pigs.

The first experiments on the common cold in human volunteers had been carried out by Dochez in America in 1930–2. These had shown that colds could be transmitted experimentally to human beings and provided the background for the English experiments. There has always been co-operation between American and English scientists in this particular field, and it was appropriate that the English work should have been carried out in a hospital sent from America as a gesture of help in the first years of the war.

In 1940 Harvard University provided and staffed a complete

E

field hospital near Salisbury for the study and treatment of any exceptional outbreaks of infectious disease that might arise in war-time England. When the United States entered the war the hospital took on normal military activities, but with the peace it was donated to the British Government with the hope that it might be used for purposes similar to those for which it was originally built. In 1946 it was decided that the hospital would provide an ideal locale for a full-scale attack on the common cold, and in the summer of that year experiments started.

I happened to be in England at the time, and one of my pleasantest memories of the visit is the week-end I spent at the Harvard Hospital with Dr Andrewes on the occasion of the very first experimental inoculations. The common cold unit was housed in a group of what were originally separate hut wards of the hospital. Each ward had been converted into a comfortable self-contained flat for two people, who for the fourteen days of their stay were forbidden any other contact with their fellows – apart from the daily inspection by the fully-gowned and masked members of the professional staff. There were indoor games, magazines, and 'Penguins', and since the hospital was on the edge of pleasant open country any pair of volunteers could take plenty of outdoor exercise provided they gave their word not to come within twenty yards of anyone encountered on their walks. No difficulty had been encountered in obtaining volunteers – the 'pairs' have even included a honeymoon couple or two! The routine is for volunteers to arrive on Saturday. They stay in isolation for four days to ensure that they are not incubating colds picked up before their arrival, and on Wednesday they are inoculated with whatever is under experiment at the time. Colds appear, if they are going to, in two to three days, and on the following Thursday all reports are complete, and after a farewell party the human guinea-pigs go home.

The experiments have nearly always taken the form of a test to determine whether or not there is living colds virus in a certain sample of fluid. The fluid might, for example, be from a chicken embryo which had been inoculated three to five days previously with filtered colds virus. If the virus could grow in such embryos this would represent a most important advance in knowledge and the answer would be sought in the following fashion. Three fluids would be prepared: (1) the 'positive control', a washing from a person with a typical cold, which would be relied on to produce colds in 60 per cent of people inoculated; (2) the 'experimental material', a solution of ground-up tissue from the chick embryos in which the virus might have grown; and (3) the 'negative control', a similar preparation from chick embryos that had never been inoculated with anything. Each of these fluids would be run into the noses of three pairs of volunteers, but none of the volunteers nor the doctor, who would assess and record their symptoms, would be told which fluid any individual had received. That information is kept private to the doctor in charge of the experiments until the results – cold or no cold – had been written down for each volunteer. It is only too easy for victim or doctor to deceive himself as to whether he has a cold or not and whether such-and-such treatment has benefited the cold, and every care must be taken to ensure that all judgements are strictly objective.

Up to the present the investigation has given what in some ways are rather disappointing results, but it is much better to know definitely that this or that is not the case than to have a vague notion that it might be and base all sorts of preventive or curative treatment on a misconception. No way of preventing or curing the common cold has yet emerged – and maybe it never will. But here are some of the conclusions that have been drawn from the experiments at Salisbury.

(a) Some, perhaps all, typical colds are due to a virus which can be proved by filtering methods to be somewhat smaller than the influenza virus, i.e. with a diameter less than 1/10,000 of a millimetre.

(b) The virus produces mild colds in about 55 per cent of people inoculated; those who fail to 'take' are presumably resistant because of immunity resulting from past colds.

(c) Probably all people living in cities are more or less immunized against colds but can be infected on the average two or three times a year. It is not possible to show that an experimental cold produces any lasting resistance to another experimental infection.

(d) The virus will not produce colds in any animal that has been tested, and a very wide range of species has been used. In America it was found that chimpanzees are susceptible.

(e) The cold virus will not grow in chick embryos.

(f) Anti-histamine drugs – widely heralded as a cure for colds – have no effect in prevention or cure.

This is not an encouraging list of conclusions, and some virologists do not feel that the experiments at Salisbury have said the last word about the common cold. For practical reasons it is necessary to work either with a single 'strain' of virus or at least with not more than two or three. Now at the present time we have no knowledge whatever as to whether there are a dozen different cold viruses or only one, but I should expect a dozen would be more likely than that all infectious colds were due to the same germ. Conclusions based like the English experiments mainly on their one 'pedigreed' strain of colds virus may not necessarily be applicable to other strains.

With the recent interest in tissue culture, strenuous efforts have been made to grow the common cold virus on various sorts of human cells, and towards the end of 1953 the Harvard

Hospital workers reported that the virus had multiplied in cultures of human embryo lung. The experiment did not always succeed and, as yet, the result is no more than a pointer to the direction in which an effective method of handling the problem may be found. The 'cytopathogenic respiratory viruses' mentioned a few pages back are apparently not responsible for the common cold.

Amongst laboratory men it is generally felt that the tissue culture of human cells will eventually give the answer to the problem of isolating those still unknown viruses which are responsible for colds and other more or less trivial human ills. The viruses may be too weakly virulent to produce gross changes in the infected cells but, by the use of two newly-developed laboratory tricks, it may still be possible to see to what extent the virus has grown.

The first of these, due to Dulbecco, makes use of an extensive flat sheet of cells on which minute amounts of virus are deposited. On such a sheet of susceptible growing cells an active virus will gradually give rise to a circular area of dead cells (a plaque) and the number of such plaques will be a measure of the amount of virus added. If the virus multiplied but did not kill the cells we should still have these small circular areas of ininfected cells. The problem would then be to 'develop' the plate so that the latent plaques could be seen and counted. One way in which this might be done makes use of the corresponding antibody to the virus. Coons of Harvard has developed a method of combining a fluorescent dye with antibody so as to make as it were a specific reagent for detecting the presence of even minute amounts of the corresponding antigen. If the antigen is a virus the dye-laden antibody will be concentrated in those cells in which the virus has multiplied. If it is flooded over a mixture of cells, some infected and some uninfected, and examined under the microscope with suitable illumination, the infected cells will be seen to glow against the unlit normal cells.

With plates carrying sheets of tissue culture cells the fluorescent-antibody will accumulate in any infected areas. Under ultra-violet light these should be visible to the naked eye as brightly-lit plaques. After such treatment of the plate on which our hypothetical virus had multiplied, the plaques should stand out clearly to the naked eye as fluorescent areas when the plate is examined under an ultra-violet lamp. But it should be stressed that no such method has been reported as successfully applied to the common cold virus up to the middle of 1954.

Set laboratory experiments on the common cold have therefore not yet told us very much. In some ways more information has been obtained from the observation of what happens in regard to colds when people are isolated from civilization for long periods.

A year or two before 1939 an American group of investigators spent a winter in Spitsbergen to see what happened in an Arctic island completely isolated from the rest of the world for eight months of the year. They found that colds broke out soon after the arrival of the first ship of the summer from outside, spread widely through the community and disappeared before the beginning of winter. During the height of the winter the resident population was segregated into three or four small communities each with no contact beyond its own members. Each group remained free from colds until spring made it possible for members of different communities to meet each other again. This was followed by a crop of mild colds, after which colds disappeared again until the arrival of the first ship of the season.

Arctic expeditions tell much the same story. After being absent for a month from civilization colds vanish for the duration of the expedition and break out again soon after contact is re-established with the rest of the world. A common embellishment to these travellers' tales is the story that the opening of a case of clothes or blankets was followed by an outbreak of colds. There is still an opportunity for someone to provide better documentation to such stories, but there seems to be no doubt about the broad facts. After a sufficient period of isolation any small group of men will rid themselves of any colds viruses that may have been initially present. Subsequently they become progressively more and more susceptible to infection by any such viruses with which they may come in contact. The other side of the story is that in any community that is not isolated from the general herd most individuals must be reinfected with colds viruses of one sort or another at frequent intervals for the most part without suffering symptoms of any sort. This constant reinfection has two results. It maintains the individual in a state of partial immunity against colds viruses in general, i.e. immunity against their power to produce symptoms, and at the same time makes him a menace to the highly susceptible person returning from twelve months in the Antarctic. These deductions might have to be modified when we have an easy way of detecting and characterizing colds viruses, but they seem to be valid at present.

This interpretation of the situation brings us back to the old jibe about the doctor's inability to do anything about the common cold. It is obvious that we are not going to eliminate colds viruses, and it is equally unlikely that any method of immunization would be more effective than the process that is at work all the time in every city dweller. In the absence of any specific drug there is very little else that seems worth trying, and my own conclusion would be that the common cold is an inescapable concomitant of urban existence.

There is one other feature which leads perhaps to an undue concentration of attention on our failure to prevent or cure colds. Any intelligent doctor will admit that there are many traditional treatments for relatively minor human ills which he uses without having any confidence that they are of real value. It is not an easy matter to establish by a valid scientific method that such-and-such a treatment regularly or usually benefits a given illness. It would be extremely difficult, for instance, to prove by a properly controlled experiment whether a purgative given at the commencement of any fever was useful or not. But when we deal with the common cold things are different. In any medical school a bacteriologist or a physician with an idea about how colds might be prevented can find with ease 200 volunteers from students and young graduates. The technique of the test is now standardized. Suppose the idea is that taking a daily tablet of drug x will prevent colds. The first move is to prepare an adequate stock of tablets, 30,000 let us say, together with another set of 30,000 tablets which look and taste just like tablets of x but contain something inactive and harmless like sugar or chalk. The stocks are then labelled A and B by someone who takes no further part in the actual experiment. Neither those who give out the tablets nor those who swallow them must know which are the 'proper' tablets, for it is rather easy to think that a cold is milder or more severe if one knows which it 'ought' to be. The 200 volunteers are divided into two groups of 100 by some method that ensures a random sample, e.g. by putting those whose birthday is on an odd-numbered day of the month in Group A and those with an even-numbered birthday in Group B. When the division has been made a statistician runs over the figures in regard to age, sex, country-born or city-bred, and anything else that may be relevant or possibly relevant, to make sure that the two groups are really equivalent. Then for a year group A takes one tablet A each day, group B one tablet B. All colds are reported and checked by a physician. At the end of the experiment we have the number of colds reported by each subject and when they occurred. The total of colds in each group is added up and the standard statistical tests applied to see whether any difference between the two is significant in the statistician's sense. Only at this stage is the man who labelled the tablets A and B called back into the picture. All the results having been recorded and analysed without bias, he can now say which were the real tablets that were supposed to prevent colds.

In all the experiments of this sort that have been reported the results have been unequivocally negative. Those which seemed hopeful have always on repetition given a negative result. Things tried have included vaccines given under the skin or by mouth, vitamins, vitamin C alone or mixed vitamins, a drug from the penicillin mould, differing from penicillin, several antihistamine drugs, and most recently aureomycin. By such tests we can say quite definitely that each of these has no action in preventing colds.

Incidentally it should be stressed that it is only by the use of this type of procedure – the 'controlled clinical trial' of medical scientists – that it was possible to say that the sulpha drugs and penicillin were effective cures for various bacterial infections. The two requirements in any test of a new method in medicine are adequate safeguards against psychological bias on the part of patient or doctor and full statistical analysis of the results. If those are fulfilled the answer will be definite and reliable.

CHAPTER TEN

GERMAN MEASLES IN PREGNANCY

FOR many years german measles (rubella) was regarded as the most benign of all the infectious fevers of childhood. Until 1941 almost every text-book of medicine concluded its brief account of the disease with the statement that there were no complications to german measles and that no special treatment of the patient was called for. In 1941, however, an Australian eye-specialist, Dr N. M. Gregg, made the very important discovery that when a woman in the early stages of pregnancy suffered an attack of rubella there was a high probability that the child would be born suffering from severe congenital damage.

In the early months of 1941 Dr Gregg found that a most unusual number of babies showing an opacity in one or both lenses of the eye were being brought to his consulting-room. The condition was one that he had hardly ever seen before, and it was obvious that something special must have been responsible for the sudden influx of patients. The eye changes were present at birth, so it was natural to enquire about anything unusual that had occurred during the mother's pregnancy. In almost every case his enquiries showed that the only thing unusual was an attack of german measles in the first, second, or third month of pregnancy.

Gregg was interested chiefly in the eyes, but he noticed also that most of the babies were poorly developed and several showed the typical signs of congenital disease of the heart – they were 'blue babies'. Once the significance of the association of german measles in pregnancy with congenital defects had been grasped, other Australian physicians soon found that in addition to the eye opacities (congenital cataract) and the congenital heart changes an even commoner result was congenital deafness and the resulting failure to talk. In the light of subsequent studies of all these damaged children it seems probable that in the early years of the Second World War about 500–600 children were born with severe congenital handicaps in Australia as a result of maternal infection with rubella. It is probable that an almost equally large number of mothers lost their baby prematurely from the same cause.

Over the years 1939–42 one could almost speak of an epidemic of antenatal rubella sweeping over Australia. It was something that had never been observed elsewhere, and the early reports from Australia were received with a good deal of incredulity both in England and America. How could one of the commonest of all infectious diseases fail to have shown this characteristic in other times and other places? The question arose whether the disease that had done such damage in Australia was really german measles or some new type of infection with similar symptoms in ordinary folk, but with a new capacity to infect the unborn child. No evidence could be found to support this idea, and nowadays it is generally accepted that it is a general character of german measles to produce the effect in a relatively large proportion of women attacked at the vulnerable stage of pregnancy.

Perhaps the most decisive evidence on this point is due to the Australian statistician, Dr H. O. Lancaster, who examined from the point of view of an epidemiologist the birth dates of people known to be congenitally deaf in Australia and New Zealand. He found, in addition to the 'epidemic' of deaf births in 1940–41, another peak in 1899 and was able to establish its relationship to very widespread epidemics of german measles in both countries towards the end of 1898. Clearly, the virus has had this capacity to damage the human embryo for a very long time.

The explanation of the exceptional incidence in Australia

was simply that in most countries the great majority of women had had an attack of rubella before the time of marriage and child-bearing, but that in Australia in 1939–42 there was a quite unusually large number of young women who had never experienced the disease. One attack of german measles usually results in immunity against a second attack, perhaps with not so great a regularity as is the case with measles proper, but enough to ensure that it is only the exceptional person who can tell of two attacks. There is also rather good evidence that some people can have a very mild infection with rubella without knowing it and subsequently be fully resistant to the disease. In Australia there was no epidemic of german measles from 1923 until a new epidemic started in Queensland in 1937. This did not spread widely until early in 1940, but then the conditions became ideal for an epidemic amongst the young adults who had grown up without a chance of becoming immune. Thousands of men were going into military camps and moving extensively from one part of the country to another. There was a sudden rise in the marriage rate, and there was an exceptionally high proportion of pregnant women in the community. The conditions were ideal for the spread of virus diseases like measles and german measles amongst the young adult population throughout Australia, and it is probable that a very large proportion of those susceptible were infected during the early war years.

In other parts of the world conditions were similar, but nowhere else was there so large a proportion of non-immunes. Careful enquiry in most countries has brought to light similar instances of congenital damage following german measles in pregnancy, but interest has nowhere been awakened to the extent shown in Australia, and most of the recent research on rubella comes from that country.

Research on german measles is not easy for the same reason that has made the study of the common cold so tedious and unproductive. It is due to a virus which can infect only human beings. This statement may not be strictly true. There have been accounts of the transfer of infection to monkeys, but symptoms were so slight that only occasionally could the experimenters feel sure that they had transmitted the disease. Unless a virus produces some reasonably obvious signs or symptoms in the animal to which it is transmitted irrespective of whether it is a monkey, mouse, or chick embryo, research along these lines is not going to tell us much. To study rubella it is necessary to have available human volunteers. Suitable volunteers are harder to find because of the requirement that they must not previously have had german measles, that they need to be isolated for two or three weeks, and that once they have assisted in one experiment they are of no value for any other. There are no such limitations in studying colds.

It is clear that when there are such difficulties to surmount, research is likely to be restricted to strictly practical matters. There is only one practical problem. What can be done to prevent the ill-effects of rubella contracted in the first three months of pregnancy? Research so far limited to Australia has been concerned only with that question.

When a woman in, say, the second month of pregnancy, suffers a typical attack of german measles there is undoubtedly a very greatly increased likelihood that the baby will suffer serious damage. Does this justify the artificial termination of the pregnancy? A very large proportion of obstetricians in Australia and America think that it does – an even larger proportion of young married people in Australia are of the same opinion. This raises some very important social and legal questions which up to the present have not been resolved – or even explicitly stated.

Royal Commissions on population problems in England and Sweden have accepted the existence and the desirability of the planned family in which children are born at the times desired and in number sufficient only to maintain a stable population. In any community which accepts such a social policy it is a logical corollary that every effort must be made to ensure the successful outcome of each pregnancy. The discovery within recent years of two intra-uterine diseases which may seriously damage the unborn child, rubella and a much rarer condition toxoplasmosis, makes it urgent to consider whether within each country where family planning is accepted as a social desideratum special notice should not be taken of their implications and the necessary changes be made in the law dealing with abortion. It may well be suggested that it is every woman's right that her pregnancy should be terminated whenever circumstances arise which in the light of current medical knowledge significantly increase the likelihood that her child will not be a socially useful and potentially happy member of the community. It will probably never be possible to say with complete certainty that any pregnancy will result in an unblemished child. There is an overall risk of something like 1 : 250 that a newly-born child will show some type of gross congenital abnormality. With healthy parents of good heredity the risk is probably much smaller, but it is never zero. Only a significantly greater probability than this normal risk can be considered.

The implementation of such a policy in regard to rubella calls for a clear statement as to the actual risk to the embryo that is associated with an attack of the disease at the various stages of pregnancy. Unfortunately, it is not yet possible to make more than a very broad estimate of these probabilities. We have some accurate figures. For instance, of some 400 instances of children born with the typical forms of congenital damage the times of the mother's illness in relation to the months of her pregnancy were as follows:

First month	90
Second month	150

Third month	105
Fourth month	44
Later months	Insignificant numbers

On the probable assumption that the number of attacks of german measles is the same in each month we can say at once that the risk of having a physically handicapped child is greatest in the second month, not much less in the third and much reduced in the fourth. From about the middle of the fourth month there is no additional risk of damage. Most doctors think that the lower figures for the first month mean only that a large proportion of the embryos infected are lost early in pregnancy.

What we do not know is in how many instances *no* damage results from an attack of rubella in the vulnerable first months. I think most of those who have studied the problem would agree that a likely figure is that 25–50 per cent of attacks in the first two months of pregnancy will result in either death of the embryo or in the birth of a congenitally abnormal child. Some authorities, however, think the figure is close to 85 per cent. From our present point of view, however, there is unanimity that an attack of rubella in the first 100 days of pregnancy greatly decreases the likelihood that a healthy unblemished child will be born.

Before leaving this problem it is desirable to point out that there is at present no conceivable way in which the damage produced by the infection in the embryo can be mitigated or cured. There is, however, one point where the filling of one of the gaps in our knowledge might enable us to diminish the incidence of damage to the child. The virus circulating in the blood of the mother when her rash is appearing has to pass through a rather complex barrier before it enters the blood of the embryo. The blood of the baby in the womb is not the mother's blood – all the nutriment for the embryo diffuses from the mother's blood across the membranes of the placenta. It is probably rather difficult for a virus to traverse this membrane, and it might be possible to make it so difficult that, despite the mother's attack, the embryo remained unscathed. We do not know how to do this, but some day research on the mechanism of the embryonic circulation may provide the knowledge.

If we can do so little once the mother is infected, we must obviously try to find means by which we can protect her from rubella during the vulnerable period of the first three months. Now, there is one absurdly simple but not always practical way of doing this – by ensuring that every girl has had an ordinary attack of german measles before marriage. In Australia at least you will find that any doctor who has a daughter will do his utmost to see that if some other member of the family has rubella she gets it too!

In Melbourne Dr S. G. Anderson carried out some important experiments that were designed to see whether it was practical to infect young women volunteers deliberately with rubella so as to provide them with this safeguard against a possible heart-breaking experience in future married life.

His volunteers were women university students, and the virus used was obtained from the throat washings of a patient with the typical rash and other symptoms. The washings were treated with penicillin to inactivate any potentially harmful bacteria and administered into the nose and throat by an atomizer. For the period over which symptoms might be expected the girls were kept in isolation and under medical observation. Many of them had typical attacks of german measles, so typically mild in fact that they rarely interfered with the social or athletic amusements which made the period of isolation a very pleasant holiday for most of them. My own daughter was in the first batch of 'guinea-pigs', so that I heard more than the scientific results of the experiment!

This series of investigations by Anderson established a number of valuable points showing by direct experiment many things which previously had only been deduced from clinical observation. He showed that the virus was present in large amount in the throat at the time the rash was at its height, and that infection is readily transferred through droplets suspended in the air and inhaled. The virus was found to be filterable, and, like all other viruses, unaffected by freezing at the temperature of 'dry ice' (−76 C). No volunteer who knew she had had german measles could be infected, and amongst those who had no knowledge or recollection of a previous attack nearly half resisted experimental infection in a fashion which made it very likely that they had had for some time in the past an unnoticed (subclinical) infection. The time between giving the virus and the appearance of the german measles rash averaged sixteen days, and in two experiments it was shown that the 'artificial' attack was just as infectious by the natural route to other susceptible people as ordinary rubella.

At the time these experiments were completed it seemed that it might be a practical proposition to use this method of artificial infection to immunize any young women who thought it worth while to ask for such an insurance against calamity. A few months later, however, poliomyelitis appeared in Victoria and the risk of conveying unsuspected poliomyelitis virus along with rubella virus seemed too great to allow any continuation of the work. The ever-present danger of all human experiments with relatively harmless viruses is this possibility that an unsuspected virus of greater potential danger may be present in the human secretion used as the source of the experimental virus. The risk is probably no greater than that accepted by anyone who travels in crowded conveyances, but it is not one that a research man or a doctor is willing to accept. For the present the only practical measure of this sort

F

will be for young women to seek out rather than avoid opportunities for natural infection with german measles.

There is one other approach to the prevention of infection in pregnancy. For many years it has been common practice to protect delicate children against measles, introduced into the family by a brother or sister, through the use of immune serum. In its most modern guise blood from people who have had measles in the past is treated in such a way to concentrate the fraction containing the protective antibody. This fraction is called gamma globulin – for reasons that are here irrelevant. A small dose is injected under the skin as soon as possible after the child has been exposed to infection. In the great majority of children given the gamma globulin in adequate dose and at the right time, no measles develop. It is only a short-lasting protection, but often one of the greatest value to a delicate or sickly child.

There seemed no reason why the same principle should not be applied to the protection of women who knew they were exposed to rubella at a dangerous period of pregnancy. Between 1948 and 1953 rather extensive tests of the method were made with generally disappointing results. There is one convenient way in which a large supply of immune serum can be obtained. German measles epidemics have a habit of appearing in military camps or naval training establishments amongst the eighteen- to twenty-year-old recruits. When this occurs there is never any difficulty in persuading a large proportion of the convalescent patients to donate a pint of blood at a time when the protective antibody is at its highest level. First from a naval depot and later from an army signals school, such supplies of convalescent serum were obtained and the antibody-containing gamma globulin prepared. Any woman in the vulnerable stage of pregnancy whose doctor knew or feared that she had been in close contact with the german measles was given an injection of 2 c.c., later 4 c.c. of the gamma globulin solution. In three years about 1,100 women were given the protective injections. Reports as to whether or not german measles followed exposure were obtained from 776 of them; 9 had had typical attacks of rubella. Superficially this suggested that the method might be valuable but, of course, there was no satisfactory evidence as to how intimate the contact with infection had been in those for whom protection might be claimed. Controlled experiments in non-pregnant subjects showed that the gamma globulin was either inert or had so weak a protective power that it could not be recognized with the relatively small number of volunteer subjects used in the two experiments that were done. This was a thoroughly disappointing experience. There is so much unhappiness in the family with a congenitally damaged child that anything which may prevent such a calamity is eagerly seized on by both patient and doctor. By all analogies gamma globulin should have been of value and there is no doubt that the injections contributed greatly to the peace of mind of many mothers. However, it is not justifiable to continue something that has been proved valueless and until new experimental work reopens the question no further use of gamma globulin for this purpose is likely in Australia.

CHAPTER ELEVEN

PSITTACOSIS

ONE of the disadvantages of knowing too much about infectious disease is that one begins to suspect even the most innocent-seeming pets of being carriers of this or that disease. It seems appropriate enough that the rat should be a potential host of plague or typhus, but it is another matter when we begin to suspect our dog of harbouring hydatids, or our pair of budgerigars as a source of that unpleasant disease psittacosis. Fortunately both of these diseases are rare, but both may be very serious to anyone unfortunate enough to be infected. Hydatid disease is, of course, due to a species of tapeworm and has no interest for us here, but psittacosis—parrot fever—is due to a virus. It is a very interesting disease from the point of view of the laboratory worker or of the public health administrator, and now that effective drugs are available for its treatment, correct diagnosis of the human illness is important to the practising doctor.

As far as I can find, the first clearly described epidemic of psittacosis occurred in Germany in the 1880's. The occasion had a bizarre quality rather frequently encountered in stories about psittacosis. The four or five people concerned had come together for supper after a funeral, and in the room where they and another dozen or more people were gathered there was a sick parakeet, almost certainly an Australian budgerigar, which, at that period, was becoming a popular cage bird. The patients were severely ill with a type of pneumonia, less acute but more prolonged than ordinary pneumonia, and it was recognized that in all probability this was an unusual infection in some way related to the sickness of the parakeet.

Occasional episodes of similar character were reported up to 1930, and some bacteriological investigations were made which suggested that a rather common type of bacterium was responsible. Then in 1930 the disease suddenly became important when several consignments of parrots from Argentina reached Europe and North America and gave rise to large numbers of human infections, many of which were fatal. Just what happened in Argentina is not quite clear, but it is known that evidence of psittacosis was observed in 1929. The most dramatic episode (in two senses!) was the infection of twelve members of a theatrical troupe following the use of a parrot on the stage in July, 1929. Two of those who were infected died. It is clear that psittacosis became widespread amongst the parrots collected for export to Europe and the most reasonable assumption is that the disease spread amongst the captive birds from one particular source. Most strains of psittacosis virus are of low virulence for man. The fact that nearly all the parrots sent to Europe in 1930 were capable of initiating severe psittacosis in human beings is the main reason for thinking that the virus concerned all came from a common ultimate source.

Many of the 1930 patients both in Europe and America were investigated by competent bacteriologists, and three research men almost simultaneously in England, Germany, and America showed that the infection was caused not by a bacterium, but by a virus. At least it was expedient at that time to call the germ responsible a virus; nowadays we are a little uncertain as to whether this is quite correct and I shall say something about the 'missing link' quality of psittacosis virus later.

Out of this work there emerged methods by which the disease could be diagnosed in human patients or in the birds that were suspected of infecting them. As usual, the white mouse provided the first means of isolating the virus and soon afterwards psittacosis virus was found to grow in the chick embryo. Large amounts of virus are produced, particularly in the yolk sac of the embryo, and from such infected tissues it was possible to prepare relatively pure virus to be used in testing blood for antibody. In psittacosis, as in herpes, and in fact nearly all infectious diseases, the presence of antibody to a given virus or other microbe means that the person or animal providing the blood has been infected by that germ. Once we have those two weapons, a means of isolating and recognizing the virus, and a means of detecting antibody in the blood, it is always possible to hope for an effective attack on any disease. Psittacosis was no exception.

So far we have been concerned with diseases that involved only human beings; here we meet what is known to epidemiologists as the animal reservoir. It is very rare for a patient with psittacosis to transmit the disease to anyone else. Ninety-nine per cent of cases pick up their infection from birds of one sort or another. To understand the disease, therefore, we have first of all to find what sort of birds are infected, how it is passed from one bird to another, and what effect it has on the birds. Then as we approach the human disease we want to know how we can recognize that a bird is infected and how the virus passes from bird to human.

The parrot disease

Right in the centre of the story of psittacosis is the Australian budgerigar (*Melopsittacus undulatus*), also called the shell parakeet or love-bird. In its wild state this is a pretty little parakeet closely barred in light green and brown with splashes of blue and yellow on wings and belly. It lives in the semi-arid country of the interior and moves in flocks, which on occasion may contain many thousands of birds. The budgerigar breeds easily in captivity and in the second half of the nineteenth century became a popular cage bird. Fanciers found that variations in the tone of the plumage could often be observed amongst the young, and particularly in Japan a wide range of colour varieties was developed by selective breeding – white, grey, mauve, and yellow as well as the natural green.

In America in the 1930s budgerigar breeding had become a flourishing minor industry with its centre in California. From here they were exported to other states and sold in department stores. In 1933 a group of human cases of psittacosis arose from contact with budgerigars in a Pittsburgh store. These birds were of Californian origin, and it became necessary to investigate what was happening in the budgerigar aviaries in that State.

Dr Karl Meyer of the Hooper Foundation in San Francisco undertook the investigation, and within a few years he had obtained a clear enough picture of the situation to allow the application of measures which temporarily at least eliminated psittacosis from the breeding establishments. He found immediately that more than half the aviaries were infected, many of them very heavily. In a badly infected aviary there would be a considerable number of deaths among young birds in the fledgling stage, while other youngsters would be obviously sick for a week or two, but recover. Most adult parakeets looked healthy, and there were only occasional deaths that could be ascribed to psittacosis.

Infection usually occurred in the nest from the droppings of the mother bird. In the young the virus passes into the blood and produces an illness of varying severity; damage may be produced in many organs and the virus passes out in droppings or in the bird's equivalent of saliva. If recovery follows, the virus tends to remain longer in the spleen and kidney than in other organs, sometimes persisting there indefinitely. An enlarged spleen in a budgerigar is a presumptive sign of past psittacosis. There is some evidence that latent infection in a recovered bird can be provoked into activity by the physiological changes that take place at egg-laying. Excretion of the virus at this time will, of course, allow infection of the next generation and so the indefinite survival of the virus in the aviary. Probably this recrudescence occurs only in a proportion of recovered birds, because everything suggests that both in the wild and in infected aviaries a certain proportion of young birds escape infection completely.

The nest is not the only place in which infection can occur. An adult bird can be infected from another, and it is not uncommon to hear that the introduction of a new bird into a cage of healthy budgerigars is followed by the death of some of the original occupants.

This work of Dr Meyer's answered the question of how psittacosis occurred in California and provided means of eliminating infected birds and re-establishing healthy breeding stock. But one important question remained – where did the psittacosis virus orginally come from? Was it present in wild Australian budgerigars? A consignment of budgerigars was, therefore, obtained from South Australia, birds which had been caught in the bush and kept from contact with any cage-bred birds. Psittacosis was present without symptoms in some of these budgerigars.

It had been believed in Australia that we had no psittacosis in our parrots, but just about the same time as Meyer's results became known word also came to Australia that some consignments of Australian cockatoos and parrots had reached Britain heavily infected with the disease. There was obviously a need for investigations to be carried out on the spot into the situation amongst Australian parrots. I undertook this work in 1935, and for two years consignments of brightly coloured birds flowed into my laboratory for investigation. The results were surprising but definite. Every common species showed a proportion of individuals infected with psittacosis that had been contracted in the wild. There is a wide variety of birds of the parrot families in Australia. Amongst species harbouring the virus were cockatoos – the white, yellow-crested cockatoo and the grey rose-breasted galah, the brilliantly coloured red, yellow, and green lorikeets, and many species of parrots and parakeets. With only an occasional exception, the birds appeared to be healthy, but there were always some from whose spleens virus could be isolated.

At the same time as this survey was going on a watch was kept for cases of human psittacosis, and for any epidemics of disease amongst parrots, either in aviaries or in the bush. Both were found. Each human case needed the exercise of a little detective ability and tact to find out what had been the effective contact with parrots and to obtain the suspected bird for examination. Everyone who has been concerned with this type of investigation will have interesting stories to tell. One of our human cases was a woman in hospital with a severe pneumonia who volunteered the information that her husband occasionally did a bit of dealing in cockatoos and that some of the birds had been dying lately. A visit to his establishment disclosed a veritable plague spot which was subsequently shown to have been responsible for three other severe infections and eight milder ones. In the backyard there were a dozen white cockatoos with soiled and bedraggled plumage and none of the inquisitive vivacity of a healthy cockatoo. The indications were unmistakable that they were infected with psittacosis, but the matter had, of course, to be clinched in the laboratory.

It can be understood that on the feathers of a sick bird there is often a great deal of dried virus to be shaken into the air if the parrot flutters or struggles. It is in fact quite a dangerous task to kill a bird showing symptoms of psittacosis.

The most practical solution is to drown the sick bird by complete immersion in a weak antiseptic solution, preferably with a cloth around the wings to prevent fluttering and splashing.

These particular cockatoos were 'textbook specimens' of advanced psittacosis, the organs were packed with virus, and it was easy to realize what dangerous spreaders of infection they could be.

Thanks to the work of Dame Jean Macnamara this particular episode was very thoroughly investigated. She found the patients and the sick cockatoos, talked to the dealers and sub-dealers in cockatoos, and followed the trail back to where the birds had been caught. I did the laboratory job of isolating and identifying the virus from patients or cockatoos. The story that ultimately emerged was this.

The sulphur-crested cockatoo is a very popular pet in Australia. It is a companionable bird and a good talker, with a tendency to attacks of bad temper, and very much an individualist. There is a brisk little trade in summer of supplying young birds for the market.

Cockatoos nest in hollows in tall eucalyptus trees, and there are some districts which are favoured nesting-places. In one of these about a hundred miles north-west of Melbourne there were four or five local men who made a few extra pounds each summer by supplying young cockatoos to Melbourne dealers. The catchers examine the nesting hollows in October and November, and when they judge that the young (one to three in each nest) are old enough, they are removed from the nests and sent in crates to the city. The birds in which we were interested had appeared to be healthy when they arrived, but within three weeks some were obviously sick. They were kept under very unsatisfactory conditions in a small dark shed in the back yard and the dealer was making every effort to sell them as quickly as possible. The severe illness of the dealer's wife and mother-in-law with mild attacks of probable psittacosis in two of his children led to our investigation and the summary destruction of all the cockatoos that could be traced. Three other households contributed eight human cases of psittacosis derived from this group of cockatoos.

By the time the investigation had clarified the position the catching season proper was over, but we managed to obtain sixteen young white cockatoos from the same district and from the same catcher. These birds were two to three months older and at the stage of leaving the nest. They were healthy in appearance, but when their organs were examined there was evidence that most of them had recovered from a mild psittacosis infection. No virus, however, could be isolated, and that interpretation of the appearances was therefore only presumptive. Taking all the evidence together we can say that, just as with Dr Meyer's Californian budgerigars, these young cockatoos were infected from their parents in the nest and would normally expect to recover completely by the time they were ready to fly. When, however, they were caged and badly fed at a time when the mild natural infection was still active, the balance was tipped against the birds' defences and in favour of the virus. Most of those cockatoos in the backyard shed were probably infected by virus they had received in the nesting hollow, but a few may have been directly infected after capture by other birds of the group.

One of the most interesting episodes of the whole investigation did not involve human beings at all. This was a widespread outbreak of fatal psittacosis in wild free-living birds over South-eastern Australia and Tasmania in 1937. Many thousands of birds must have died, probably millions in South Australia, and sick or recently dead birds picked up in three states, South Australia, Victoria, and Tasmania, were all proved to be infected with acute psittacosis. This could only have meant that during that year an unusually virulent type of the virus had appeared in one of the common parrots and that it had spread widely amongst non-immune adult birds. In the ordinary course nest infection gives rise to a mild infection only which will immunize the bird against a subsequent infection by a more virulent type of virus. There is much variation in the proportion of parrots showing signs of nest infection, and we can be sure that on occasion large numbers may fail to be infected and provide a big susceptible population. The combination, however, of a highly lethal virus and a large population of non-immune parrots must be a very rare one, since the 1937 outbreak is the only time that widespread death of parrots in the wild has been reported.

Psittacosis in Seabirds and others

There is another story of psittacosis with a very different setting from the Australian bush. The Faeroe Islands, in the North Atlantic, provide a thousand or two people with a meagre living, and offer nesting places to millions of seabirds. The fulmar petrel has for the last hundred years been increasing in number and extending its nesting range in the North Atlantic. It has been established for many years in the Faeroes, and the islanders by 1933 had become used to preparing large numbers of young fulmars for food. The young birds, well developed and fat, but still unable to fly, were collected on the nesting cliffs by the men and taken to small huts where they were plucked and pickled by the women. From 1933 onwards physicians on the islands found that severe attacks of pneumonia were occurring, almost all in women, at the period when the young fulmars were being taken. In 1938 the suspicion that the disease was psittacosis led to investigations being made by German bacteriologists which uncovered essentially the same pattern as had been observed in budgerigars and cockatoos. Infection of the young bird from the parents was normally followed by recovery, but many of the fledglings taken to the plucking sheds were still excreting virus and soiling their feathers and down. As the birds were plucked, virus-contaminated dust was liberated into the air and inhaled by the workers. Human psittacosis is always a lung infection, and when the virus inhaled is of sufficient virulence the result of its multiplication is manifested as pneumonia. Once the origin of these cases of 'summer pneumonia' in the Faeroes had been established a ban was placed on the handling of young fulmars and the disease has virtually disappeared.

There are some interesting ornithological sidelights on this story. The fulmar petrels were apparently evolved in the Southern hemisphere, and for many years had only two breeding places in the North Atlantic, one the island of St Kilda, the second on an island off Iceland. Only in the nineteenth century were the Faeroes colonized. In most of the islands concerned young birds were used as food as soon as they become plentiful enough, and in none did psittacosis appear till 1931 in the Faeroes. There was none on St Kilda up to the time the island was evacuated finally in 1930. Some virologists are disposed to credit a story that in 1930 a Danish ship threw overboard near the Faeroes a number of sick or dead Argentine parrots and that scavenging fulmars may have become infected from these. Many other seabirds are known to have their own infections with psittacosis-like viruses, and it is perhaps rather improbable that we could pinpoint the first infection of a new species in this spectacular fashion. The strongest piece of circumstantial evidence is that the Faeroe Island fulmars are the only birds outside of the parrot family which carry a virus that behaves in laboratory tests like a parrot virus and has a relatively high virulence for man.

When methods of isolating the virus and of making blood tests for evidence of past infection with psittacosis had been

developed and made readily available to physicians, and especially when doctors had become widely aware of the existence
of the disease, cases began to be recognized in persons having
no contact with parrots or petrels. More and more birds were
found to be infected with a virus which could, usually with
some difficulty, produce experimental psittacosis in mice and
which on occasion gave rise to human infection. In the
medical literature one can read stories of how city pigeons in
Liverpool, in Melbourne, in Johannesburg, or in Cincinnati
have been shown to be infected with something which, because they are not parrots, is called ornithosis virus. It is
quite indistinguishable from a low virulence strain of psittacosis, and it is probable that city pigeons everywhere in the
world are infected.

So far the domestic fowl appears to be almost completely
innocent, but in the mammoth duck farms of Long Island,
N.Y., there have been cases of infection amongst people
handling the ducks.

The last outbreak of disease of this type that need be mentioned is one that took place in the Bayou region of Louisiana
in 1943. A hunter who had been recently handling a variety
of wild birds became seriously ill and was hospitalized. He
transmitted the infection to three of his hospital attendants
and initiated a chain of sick-bed transfers of infection involving nineteen persons with eight deaths. A typical psittacosis virus was isolated from the patients, but its final origin
was never determined. On a number of other occasions a
similar chain of patient to nurse or doctor infections by
psittacosis viruses has been observed.

Sometimes one is moved to wonder whether a particular
type of psittacosis virus may not some day cut itself adrift
from the birds in which it evolved and embark on a new career
as a producer of human disease easily transmissible from man
to man.

CHAPTER TWELVE

SMALLPOX AND VACCINATION

THERE are two of the great historic plagues that are due to viruses, yellow fever and smallpox. Yellow fever has never made more than occasional sorties beyond the tropics and subtropics, but smallpox in its time has raged over every climate. For nearly 200 years the possibilities of preventing smallpox by this or that manipulation, variolation, or vaccination were matters of acute controversy, and it is probably true that the early development of the science of immunity was predominantly influenced by Jenner's discovery of vaccination. There are still echoes of controversy – antivaccinationists are not yet convinced of anything but the occasional harmful accident associated with vaccination – but to the best of my belief there is no sane man with a reasonably adequate knowledge of the facts who does not recognize that the elimination of smallpox as a serious disease from Western civilization was due far more to vaccination than to any other factor.

Smallpox in its classical form still to be seen in the East is a repulsive disease with a high mortality. It comes on as an acute prostrating fever and headache without at first any sign of a rash. This appears about a day later as firm nodules in the skin, especially of the face and hands. The nodules enlarge and soften and within a week may become filled with pus. At the height of the disease the whole face may be covered with a confluent mass of blisters and pustules, while the rest of the body is heavily but not quite so closely spattered with similar pocks. In the most acute form of the disease, haemorrhagic or 'black' smallpox, the rash is replaced by bleeding into the skin and early death is invariable.

If the patient with the more normal form of smallpox recovers, the pocks gradually dry up and scab off, leaving the characteristic pitted scars. Once recovery has been achieved the patient is completely insusceptible to further infection by the virus and this immunity lasts for life.

Very few diseases show the regularity of measles or chickenpox, in which any epidemic is essentially the same as any other epidemic of the same disease. Smallpox epidemics vary greatly in the average severity of the infections produced. In addition to the classical severe disease there is a milder form often called alastrim that was common both in England and America during the twenties and thirties of this century, but was also known many years earlier. Except in persons sick from some other cause as well, this variant of smallpox is as trivial a disease as chickenpox. Nevertheless it *is* smallpox, the pocks, though few in number, are of the same type, an attack of alastrim makes a person immune to typical smallpox, and vaccination protects against either.

The history of smallpox gives the impression that the disease has flared up most irregularly over time and place. In England for instance the eighteenth century was the only period when smallpox was a universal and dangerous disease, yet 200 years earlier it had swept through Mexico with Cortez, producing enormous mortality amongst the Mexicans, and still earlier was recorded by Arabic writers as afflicting an Ethiopian army at the siege of Mecca in A.D. 569. It is rather likely that some gaps in the history of smallpox mean simply that at that particular time a mild variant of the disease was current, unnoticed by lay and medical chroniclers, and that it provided immunity against any more virulent strain of the virus that might be introduced. On this view apparent absence of smallpox epidemics in the days before Jenner might have had essentially the same explanation as its decrease in the nineteenth century – natural or deliberate infection with a similar virus of low virulence (alastrim or vaccinia) providing immunity against smallpox. On the other hand, it is quite possible for a disease to spread epidemically and afterwards to disappear completely from the country concerned. Other periods of reputed freedom from smallpox may have been associated with actual absence of the virus in any form.

To appreciate the significance of Jenner's work it is necessary to have some knowledge of the extent of smallpox in England in the second half of the eighteenth century. To an epidemiologist the most striking feature of smallpox at that period was that more than 90 per cent of the cases (and deaths) in London were in children under five. This implies a universal distribution of the virus in the sense that every infant and equally of course every child and adult could expect to be exposed to infection at least once in five years. The disease behaved in fact almost precisely as measles does now, but it killed many more children and left many of those who recovered with faces pitted with scars for life. In the country smallpox was not so constantly present, and in many areas people might reach adult life without exposure. It was a common story to hear of young men and women from the country who had come to London to find death from smallpox instead of a fortune.

Since one had to have the smallpox in eighteenth-century London, there were many who argued that it was desirable that a child should have it at the time most convenient to its parents rather than wait for the inevitable chance infection. The practice of variolation was introduced from the Middle East by Lady Mary Wortley Montagu in 1718 and became immediately a topic of violent controversy in both lay and medical circles. The technique was simply to take some of the 'matter' from a pustule on a child with a mild case of smallpox and inoculate this into a scratch on the arm of the child to be variolated. Quite frequently the desired result, a local sore at the site of inoculation and a few pocks only on the rest of the body, was obtained, but there were of course sufficient accidents to keep controversy well alight.

The story of Jenner has often been told, but it is impossible to write about smallpox in English without repeating its essentials. Jenner was a country apothecary in Gloucestershire with a taste for natural history which had brought him into contact with the famous surgeon and naturalist, John Hunter. By the time of his work on vaccination Jenner had already a minor scientific reputation as an authority on the habits of the cuckoo. He had been the first to observe that the young cuckoo actually ejected the legitimate nestlings from the nest and had described a depression in the back of cuckoo which appeared to be an adaptation for this purpose. After the publication of this paper he had become a Fellow of the Royal Society. It was natural therefore that when Jenner in 1797 wrote his paper on 'An Inquiry into the Natural History of a Disease known in Glostershire by the name of the "Cowpox"' he should send it to the Royal Society. It was returned to the author with the advice that as he had gained some reputation by his former papers to the Royal Society, he should not risk losing his established credit by publishing this one! It is almost the rule for a scientific discovery later known to be of outstanding significance to be looked at askance by the established authorities at the time of its first appearance. It is also common to find that the discoverer's enthusiasm runs far beyond his evidence, and when we remember that there are a dozen heretical ideas of no importance for every one that has any significance, we should retain some of our sympathy for the sceptics. Jenner published his paper as a pamphlet in 1798, and we can probably accept Greenwood's verdict on this pamphlet, that it was 'just the sort of rambling discursive essay containing acute observations mixed up with mere conjectures which an unsystematic field naturalist might be expected to produce.'

Jenner had become aware like many other country practitioners that there was a persistent tradition that milkers who had contracted cowpox were thereby rendered incapable of taking smallpox. The sores produced by cowpox either on the cow's udder or on the milker's hands are not very unlike those of smallpox, so that if the protective effect did exist, it was something that might well be thought of by those who had had experience of both infections. Jenner's 'Inquiry' was designed to show *experimentally* two things, first that persons who had had cowpox would not take smallpox when infective matter was inoculated into the skin, and second that cowpox could be transferred at will from cow or dairymaid to children and that after artificial infection with cowpox those who were thus 'vaccinated' would resist an inoculation of smallpox. Both points were established to Jenner's satisfaction – but as a scientific paper it was definitely thin. It made a preliminary case for the use of the method of vaccination, but certainly failed to establish its value. The important thing, however, was that an idea had been put into circulation, an idea with so important a bearing on an urgent practical problem that others were almost immediately impelled to test it out.

The story of the first twenty-five years of vaccination to the time of Jenner's death in 1823 is not very flattering to the intelligence of any of those concerned. Some of the procedures in the tests of 'cowpoxing' in London are horrifying to any modern medical scientist. Most of the work was done in an Inoculation Hospital where natural smallpox, inoculation smallpox, and cowpox all flourished and where one could be certain that mixed infections were the rule. Nevertheless out of the muddle there steadily emerged the fact that vaccination did do very much what Jenner had claimed for it.

Smallpox is not a disease that thrives in progressive modern cities where there are well-equipped research laboratories and public health authorities are not enthusiastic that the virus should be brought to such laboratories from the tropical centres of the disease. Relatively little work has therefore been done during the modern (post-1930) phase of virus research on the virus of smallpox and its properties. Curiously enough, it is one of the easiest viruses to culture. In plate 4 there is a photograph of a membrane from a chick embryo on which a drop of blood from a patient in the acute stage of severe smallpox was deposited. After three days' incubation the white spots (pocks) had developed, and one can be certain that in that drop of blood there were at least the same number of virus particles. By the use of this technique of growth on the chick embryo membrane all the usual sorts of laboratory test to identify and characterize the virus can be carried out.

Typical smallpox is an easy disease to diagnose – but there are surprisingly large numbers of minor or moderately severe skin infections which may mimic or be mimicked by slightly unusual smallpox rashes. It may be a matter of great importance that an early and definite diagnosis should be made. The laboratory nowadays can be very helpful. A little fluid is scraped from a suspicious spot on the skin for examination. Part of it may be spread out on a glass slide and appropriately stained so that the virus particles stand out as very tiny red dots under a high-power microscope. An experienced bacteriologist can often be very nearly certain after examining such a slide whether the patient has or has not a true smallpox. To be certain he mixes the scraping with a little penicillin solution and drops it on to four or six chick embryo membranes. In three days he will have a definite answer from the presence or absence of pocks on the membrane. In practice things are not quite so simple. Accidents happen and delicate techniques may go awry. Sometimes every possible test is needed and the answer finally obtained only by waiting and watching for developments.

There are as yet no drugs which are directly active on the virus of smallpox or on any other virus, but penicillin has been of great value in diminishing what used to be a very distressing phase of secondary skin infection by ordinary bacteria. When there is an overwhelming infection by the virus death may occur before the rash is fully developed, and in these cases no treatment is of any avail.

Vaccination remains the sheet-anchor of smallpox control, and the methods of preparing the vaccine lymph have remained unchanged in principle for the last sixty years. Calves or sheep are inoculated on broad shaved areas of skin and when the blisters of the vaccinia rash develop the animals are killed and the virus-containing material scraped off the skin into a preservative solution containing a high percentage of glycerine. There are always some bacteria potentially capable of producing septic infection in this crude 'lymph', and various methods of getting rid of bacteria without damaging the virus have been developed. They all take time, and it is therefore impossible to provide large amounts of vaccine lymph at short notice unless very large reserve stocks are constantly maintained.

Many modern virologists have suggested that it would be far more logical to prepare vaccinia virus without any bacteria in chick embryos so that it could be used within two days of its being harvested from the eggs. The method is perfectly satisfactory but has never been developed on a large scale. The reasons are simply that the old-style calf lymph is of proved effectiveness, it can be readily prepared with relatively simple apparatus, it keeps under unfavourable conditions somewhat better than 'egg' virus, and there are well tried ways of dealing with its bacterial contaminants. If the method of vaccination against smallpox had been developed in 1948 instead of 150 years earlier I am certain that the virus would have been prepared with a careful aseptic technique in chick embryos. I suspect indeed that the modern discoverer would have shuddered at the thought of using so crude a method as the scarification of a calf's skin! It is the old story that there are nearly always at least two different ways of doing any technical operation and that none of them will work properly until the minor difficulties have been ironed out and experience has been gained in handling the process. Once one alternative has been mastered and made to work satisfactorily it is likely to persist with only slow change in detail unless one of the alternatives can show some quite outstanding advantage.

Vaccination, as we have said already, is simply the production of a localized area of skin infection with the virus of vaccinia. The requirements are that living virus particles should be brought into contact with a number of the skin cells that lie two or three layers of cells deep from the surface. The surface cells of the skin grow constantly from below and as they approach the air become dry and dead – a simple protective covering that is steadily rubbed off from the surface. The living cells needed for growth of the virus are deeper down, so that some form of pricking or scratching the skin is necessary. There are many variants of technique, but the most commonly recommended method of vaccination is to place a drop of the glycerinated lymph on the skin and press down gently through the drop with the point of a needle held horizontally against the skin. Fifteen or twenty such 'lateral pressures' are made within an area of about an eighth of an inch square. No dressing should be placed over the inoculated area.

What is really more important than the actual method of vaccination is the availability of a good active virus in the lymph. The lymph at the time it is used should contain large numbers of living virus particles, a million or more per drop. There is only one safe way to ensure this, which is to keep the vaccine lymph in a refrigerator from the time of its preparation to the hour of its use. No one has quite solved the practical problems of vaccination in the tropics.

It may be interesting at this point to consider just what vaccination amounts to in the light of modern virology. The first thing we should like to know is where the virus which is stored and produced in every vaccine lymph establishment in the world, came from. By repute it is the lineal descendant of the virus Jenner obtained from cows and dairymaids in Gloucestershire around 1796. But in the first half of the 19th century vaccination was carried out from arm to arm by hundreds of doctors none of whom had any conception of asepsis and who were mainly interested in finding a strain of 'matter' that would give consistent takes without objectionable side effects. Vaccination was often done in the presence of a beginning smallpox epidemic and smallpox virus was not uncommonly transferred instead of or as well as cowpox virus.

Eventually arm to arm vaccination was replaced completely by calf-lymph, and it appears that all the vaccinia virus current in the laboratories is probably derived from a strain transferred to calves around 1850 after a long series of arm to arm passages. The virus as we know it differs considerably from the cowpox that still exists in England and is equally distinct from smallpox virus. Professor Downie of Liverpool has compared four viruses – smallpox, vaccinia, cowpox, and mousepox – by growing them on membranes of the chick embryo. They all grow well, but the pocks produced differ characteristically for each virus. Each will produce immunity against infection by any of the others in as far as it is possible to make the tests, but the strength of the immunity varies. Judging by all the criteria that are available vaccinia virus is considerably nearer to smallpox than to cowpox virus. Most authorities think that the virus we now use for vaccination is a modified smallpox virus that has lost its power to spread through the body, and not a descendant of Jenner's cowpox.

There is plenty of evidence that vaccination has a very important effect in diminishing the likelihood of contracting smallpox after exposure to infection and increasing the chance of recovery if infection does occur. Modern research has been directed more to finding out the means by which this immunity is developed than to proving once again that it exists. One interesting approach to the problem has been that used by Dr Fenner in Melbourne. He vaccinated not men but mice. Vaccinia virus is at least as effective in vaccinating mice against mousepox as it is in human beings against smallpox. If one sets up two 'herds' of mice, one vaccinated and the other unvaccinated, and into each herd one introduces a dozen mice infected with mousepox virus, the resulting difference is something to gladden the heart of an enthusiast for vaccination. In Fenner's experiment no mice died in the vaccinated groups, and when infection occurred it could be recognized only by close study of the animals. By contrast in the unvaccinated mice there was a high mortality with almost universal evidence of infection in the survivors.

Analysis of the immunity showed that it was closely associated with the presence of antibody in the blood. The antibody produced by vaccination did not however provide so effective an immunity against mousepox as we find when a mouse survives an actual attack of the disease. In fact when the infection was studied in detail the vaccinated mice seemed only a little better able to cope with each phase than the unvaccinated. But the overall result was very striking, the difference between certain survival and a 30 per cent chance of death.

Vaccination in human beings similarly cannot be expected to produce an immunity as firm and long-lasting as that which follows an attack of smallpox. There are two requirements for the artificial production of immunity against a given disease. The first is that the quality, the individuality, the specificity of the immunizing material should be the same as that of the virus responsible for the disease. In technical language, we must have all the essential antigens of the pathogenic virus, included in or capable of being produced by the immunizing material. The second requirement is that the vaccine should be capable of providing a sufficiently active stimulus to the antibody-producing cells of the body. In general this means merely that a sufficient *amount* of each antigen is injected into or produced within the body.

On the first score vaccinia virus is very like smallpox virus, but it is not quite the same. However, as we have said, it resembles smallpox more than it does mousepox, so that, other things being equal, vaccination should be rather more effective in man than Fenner found it to be in his mice.

The question of how much antibody-stimulating material gets into the body is the important one once we are satisfied that its quality is near enough to what we want. This raises again the old dilemma in attempts to immunize against virus diseases of whether a living or a killed vaccine should be used. In vaccination we use a live virus that can multiply within the body and so build up an adequately immunizing dose. In influenza vaccination a killed virus preparation is used, and what is injected through the needle must serve. Both types have their advantages and disadvantages. In general the live virus produces a stronger immunity, but its use is subject to more accidents, most of which arise from the self-evident fact that you cannot sterilize a living virus. If by chance some other virus has slipped in somewhere along the production line, there is no automatic way of getting rid of it, and the consequences may be serious. There is practically no risk of this sort with ordinary vaccination. The calves used are always killed and examined very carefully for any other type of infection before the lymph they provide is issued. The process used in getting rid of casual bacteria will also kill nearly all potentially dangerous germs – vaccinia virus is one of the most resistant of them all – and there is a final safeguard in the method of inoculation. The superficial scratch on the skin is a rather poor method of inoculation except for viruses like vaccinia which are specially adapted to multiply in skin cells.

In the unvaccinated person, then, the virus multiplies in the deeper cells of the skin, both those that were infected with the needle and others immediately adjacent. The cells enlarge, liquefy, and break down, liberating much virus into a pool of blister fluid which accumulates under the dead outer sheet of skin cells. Virus and virus fragments pass to the lymph glands. Anyone with a vaccination at its height will find large and tender lumps in the corresponding armpit – these are inflamed lymph glands in the process of making antibody. Some virus also passes into the blood, where it normally does no harm. Antibody begins to appear in the blood about the seventh day, and in three or four days more is in sufficient amount to prevent any further development of the local sore. There is evidence that vaccination has some protective effect against smallpox for as long as thirty years, but it is the general rule to insist on revaccination every two years where people are exposed to real danger of being infected.

The response to revaccination gives quite an interesting insight into immunity. If we have a standard method of vaccination that can always be relied on, the type of response will give an accurate measure of the person's immunity in the first instance against vaccinia virus but also by implication and experience against smallpox. The completely susceptible, previously unvaccinated individual responds rather slowly, nothing definite being visible till the third or fourth day, and the full development of the blister being reached at the ninth. From the seventh to the tenth day the subject may feel moderately unwell, with fever and enlarged lymph glands. At the other extreme the man who has been vaccinated on several occasions within recent years will show a small reddish lump within a day. This enlarges a little and may look a little paler at the top but does not form a blister and is little more than a reddish brown spot on the skin after one week. Such a reaction is called an 'immune reaction', and is taken as being significant of effective immunity to smallpox. In between are all grades of intermediate reactions.

When should vaccination be carried out? In any country where there is still definite risk of contact with the disease, in infancy at about three months of age and at such subsequent times as local circumstances indicate. In Western countries where there is normally no smallpox the answer is not so easy. If millions of babies are vaccinated a few will have nasty illnesses as a result and one or two may die – If there is *no* risk of smallpox we cannot expect parents to subject their children to any sort of danger or inconvenience in an attempt to protect against a non-existent risk. As smallpox became rare at the end of the nineteenth century there was an increasing disinclination to accept compulsory vaccination, and in no Western country is universal vaccination of infants enforced at present.

Current opinion is that the only practical solution in a Western democracy is to maintain large supplies of lymph in store, to enforce vaccination of service personnel, hospital attendants of all sorts, and any others exposed to more than normal risk, and to make vaccination available to the public generally whenever smallpox enters the country. Health officers will always need to retain their present power to order the vaccination of any person known to have been in contact with a case of smallpox, but most of them feel that general vaccination of the community can safely be left till public demand arises on the entry of the disease into the country. It is a second-best policy, but it has a certain democratic justification in that there is a rough correspondence between the need for vaccination and the degree of public panic induced by the spread of the epidemic. Fortunately smallpox introduced into Western countries in the last forty or fifty years has not shown any tendency to spread beyond the possibility of control, and to that extent the present opportunist policy is justified.

CHAPTER THIRTEEN

YELLOW FEVER AND DENGUE

THERE is a broad belt round the world comprising virtually all the well-watered and inhabited parts of the tropics and subtropics within which a certain mosquito *Aedes aegypti* flourishes. In many such places it is extremely common, but it is on the whole an easy mosquito to get rid of if money and effort are forthcoming.

Aedes has been responsible for two important virus diseases – yellow fever, the great plague of West Africa and Central America in the days of the slave trade, and dengue, a disease which does not kill but which may spread in enormous epidemics and put half the population of a city out of action at one time.

In its typical form yellow fever begins suddenly with a rapidly rising temperature, shivering, and headache. The patient becomes extremely ill and three or four days from the onset is likely to vomit material containing blood and to show a sallow jaundiced appearance. These were the two standard signs of the disease in the old days, the black vomit and the yellow skin that gave yellow fever its name. Death rates used to be high and the end usually came six to eight days after the patient had become ill. If the patient survived ten days he usually made a rapid recovery and was thereafter completely immune.

In heavily infected areas, the West Indies during the nineteenth century for example, it was well known that those who had been born and bred in the country were immune to the disease. It was only the newcomer who was likely to die. The same was noticed in West Africa where the Negro appeared to be quite insusceptible to the disease that killed most white men who stayed long enough on the coast. We now know that this feature of the disease depends on the fact that children infected with the virus for the first time usually have a mild illness which leaves them immune for life. When infection occurs in an adult who has not been immunized by a previous attack symptoms are much more severe and death is frequent.

This is the aspect of yellow fever that has been responsible for most of its historical manifestations. In its home countries on either side of the Atlantic the native populations were hardly affected. The impact of the disease fell on Europeans coming as adults to these regions, especially on the soldiers and sailors sent on imperialistic adventures by the great maritime powers. One of the first records is Drake's loss of more than 200 men from what was almost certainly yellow fever when off the West Coast of Africa in 1585. The disease was closely associated with the slave trade and was the major risk to health on the Guinea Coast and in the West Indies for three centuries. During the Napoleonic wars both British and French armies were impartially destroyed by yellow fever in the West Indies and heavy toll was taken of garrison troops in the region right up to the beginning of the twentieth century.

When the disease spread beyond its home countries the incidence on the non-immune population was often disastrous. In the early years of the American colonies it reached as far north as Boston and several severe epidemics were recorded in Philadelphia and New York. Spain being well within the range of *Aedes aegypti* and with an active commerce with Central America also suffered a number of widespread outbreaks, notably in 1730 and 1800. Even England experienced one small episode of yellow fever infection on its own soil. This occurred at Swansea in 1865, some customs officers and labourers being infected, presumably by mosquitoes that had been carried on a ship from Cuba.

There is a long history of investigations into the cause and mode of transmission of yellow fever, which is rendered more than usually interesting by the danger that was associated with the work. There have been more deaths of laboratory workers from yellow fever than from any other infectious disease.

As soon as the bacterial origin of many infectious diseases had been established attempts to isolate bacteria were made from the blood of yellow fever patients. The usual variety of bacteria were found and some were thought for a time to be the cause of the disease. Around 1881 a Cuban physician Dr Carlos Finlay published a suggestion that yellow fever might be spread by a mosquito and even identified the mosquito correctly under its then name of *Culex fasciatus*. Finlay carried out a number of experimental transmissions from patient to volunteer by mosquito, but for one reason or another raised no more than an academic interest in his hypothesis. The first official interest in the cause and mode of transmission was provoked as a result of the heavy mortality from yellow fever amongst American troops in Cuba during the Spanish-American war. The U.S. army sent a Commission headed by Major Walter Reed to investigate the problem on the spot. After failing to find any evidence of the existence of the particular bacterium which in 1900 held pride of place amongst possible causes of yellow fever, they turned to Finlay's ideas as providing the best working hypothesis. It proved easy enough to confirm the significance of the mosquito in spreading the disease – all that was required was a technique of handling mosquitoes and enough volunteers to take the chance of a rapid and unpleasant death! The volunteers were forthcoming and by the beginning of 1901 all the important information about the transmission of yellow fever in the West Indies had been obtained and made public. Nothing, however, was discovered about the nature of the micro-organism responsible, and it is a curious fact that yellow fever was banished from the West Indies by specific administrative action before it was shown that a virus was the agent of the disease.

The action required was simply to make it an offence for any householder or landowner to have mosquito larvae on his premises, to educate people in how to get rid of casual collections of water or to screen those that were necessary from mosquitoes, and to police each community with well-trained sanitary inspectors. One additional measure was required, that all persons sick with yellow fever or suspected yellow fever should be screened from possible mosquitoes. If no mosquito could become infected from a human patient that would eliminate yellow fever as effectively as if all mosquitoes were exterminated. By 1925 Central America appeared to have been wholly cleared, and the only focus left in the Western hemisphere was believed to be in Brazil and due for extinction with a little further work.

In the next five years the whole picture changed. In West Africa it was shown that yellow fever could be transmitted to the common Indian monkey, producing a disease that was usually fatal and unmistakably yellow fever. Once any disease can be transferred with certainty to an experimental animal that is available in relatively large numbers, one can be certain that its nature will be elucidated within a year or two. Even if in the course of the work a dozen investigators die of the disease – and within a year of the discovery Stokes, Noguchi, and Young so died in West Africa – the answers will be obtained.

Soon the virus had been trained to grow in mice, in tissue cultures, and in chick embryos, and two important weapons were forged. The first was a means of telling whether a given person had ever had yellow fever by testing for anti-body in his blood. In principle the method was to mix blood serum from the person in question with a small standard amount of yellow fever virus and inject the mixture into six mice. If more than half the mice survived antibody was present and at some time in his life the person who provided the serum had had yellow fever.

The second weapon was an attenuated virus obtained by passage first through mice and then through tissue cultures, which could be used to immunize susceptible persons who had to work or fight in infected regions. The principles of yellow fever immunization have already been described in Chapter Five.

A third weapon for investigation and control was provided by those scientists who were interested in the changes produced in the liver of patients dying from yellow fever. The cells are strikingly modified and to an expert pathologist the changes are easily recognized as being due to yellow fever and nothing else. This offered a solution to an important problem for those concerned with the health of backward tropical countries. If a doctor or health inspector in the depths of the jungle finds that a man has just died of what may have been yellow fever, how is he to make certain? What was called a viscerotome was the answer. This is an instrument with a shielded knife that could be pushed through a small cut in the skin into the liver of the corpse. A small piece of tissue is removed by the instrument from the substance of the liver and placed in a formalin solution to preserve it till it can be sent to a laboratory and examined.

The first and third methods, the mouse protection test for antibody and the examination of viscerotome sections for evidence that death had been due to yellow fever, made it possible to map the world for the presence of the virus. As the survey took shape it became clear that the optimism of 1925

G

was wholly unwarranted. There were enormous areas where for many years at least man would have to find ways of living with the yellow fever virus. In these regions immunization could provide the only means of protection.

Classical yellow fever, the disease of tropical ports and slave ships, is a wholly human disease spread from man to man by the mosquito *Aedes aegypti*. It is as we have said an easy disease to eliminate, and it is virtually extinct. But the yellow fever of the ports is not the means by which yellow fever virus survived either in the past or in the present. The virus is really a parasite of jungle monkeys and is transmitted from one animal to another by jungle-haunting mosquitoes quite different from *Aedes*, which is very much a domestic mosquito rarely found far from human habitations. The situation is essentially similar in both the African and the Brazilian tropical rain forests, and it is not clear whether the disease arose in Africa or America. Perhaps it is equally likely that the virus has been with the monkey tribe ever since the common ancestor of the Old World and New World monkeys flourished somewhere in Asia or Africa.

Workers or travellers in the jungle may be bitten by virus-carrying jungle mosquitoes, and if they can reach a town on the seashore or in open country before becoming sick a new outbreak of classical *Aedes*-spread yellow fever may be initiated. In 1936 an actual incident of this sort was observed and verified in Brazil. Twenty-five cases in one circumscribed area of the town of Cambara were clearly traced to a labourer who had been infected while working in primeval jungle ten miles from the town. Similar episodes must have been common in the past. Most epidemiologists would agree that yellow fever of *Aedes* type could hardly continue to survive in any stable community – it would have to be fed by a constant arrival of newcomers non-immune to the disease. With the discovery of jungle yellow fever the mystery of the persistence of yellow fever over at least the last four centuries was solved. The virus persists in the monkeys of the tree-tops and the mosquitoes that bite them. It is hardly more than an accident when the disease finds new possibilities to spread in a human community.

The prevention of yellow fever now has two aspects. The old techniques that were used by Gorgas to rid Cuba of yellow fever and make it possible to build the Panama Canal still have their place in any community in the tropics that is exposed to the risk of entry of the disease. Even where continued existence of yellow fever in the jungles must be accepted a great deal can be done by *Aedes* control. Over the last decade a great effort has been made by Brazil and other South American States, assisted by the International Health Division of the Rockefeller Foundation, to achieve the total eradication of the mosquito from tropical America.

Without *Aedes* around the towns and villages, human infections will be confined to the few individuals actually infected by jungle mosquitoes. Epidemics will not occur. The use of DDT as an insecticide has made the eradication of *Aedes aegypti* mosquitoes from the whole of North and South America a possibility. This is the declared objective of the Pan-American Health Organization and, thanks to the support, financial and technical, of the Rockefeller Foundation, it was very close to achievement in 1952. In Brazil only a few foci remained in the north-eastern section of the country. Air transport has introduced an important new element into the control of yellow fever. Special precautions are now mandatory to prevent the carriage of mosquitoes by aircraft and to ensure that concentrated anti-mosquito measures are enforced around all international aerodromes.

In the areas of jungle yellow fever reliance must be chiefly on immunization. These areas are roughly as follows: – In Africa the northern boundary runs from near Dakar along the edge of the Sahara to Khartoum, then an eastern boundary follows the Upper Nile and the great lakes and a southern limit runs west from Lake Tanganyika to the coast. In America the Amazon basin is the greatest centre, but there are areas of infection throughout Central America as far north as Southern Mexico. An unsolved riddle is presented by the fact that yellow fever never reached the east coast of Africa nor spread into Asia and the East Indies, although the *Aedes* mosquito is prevalent everywhere in the tropics and there are monkeys in much of the area.

During the second world war it was thought advisable by the American Army to have all troops who might be sent to any tropical theatre of war immunized against yellow fever. There was a definite fear that with the changing circumstances of war and air transport the virus might exceed its normal bounds and reach the tropics of Eastern Asia.

With the entry of the U.S. into the war in December, 1941, immunization of service men with the 17D vaccine mentioned earlier was begun on a very large scale and continued in the first months of 1942.

In March and April 1942, about 80,000 American service men were ill with jaundice (hepatitis), which was in some way associated with the fact that they had been immunized with certain batches of yellow fever vaccine. This was the most dramatic demonstration ever given of the potential dangers of giving a living virus as an immunizing vaccine. The incriminated batches of vaccine, in addition to the 17D yellow fever virus, also contained another virus in a living condition – the virus of serum hepatitis.

We are still rather puzzled about the hepatitis viruses. There is one disease, which we call infectious hepatitis, which is the commonest cause of yellow jaundice in young people. This is due to a fairly ordinary virus which has some resemblances to poliomyelitis virus in being especially associated with the intestine. The disease is probably contracted from contaminated water or food and has the unusually long incubation period of 28–30 days. Only in a proportion of those infected does the full picture of an attack of jaundice develop; in many there is probably no more than a local infection in the bowel, with some symptomless leaking of virus into the blood.

The second disease, serum hepatitis, at the present time seems to be only a creation of the hypodermic needle, but most virologists believe that it will eventually be found related to infectious hepatitis. It is a disease with the same symptoms as the latter which comes on between two and three months after the patient has received an injection of human blood or some product prepared from human blood. We must be quite clear that only something in the neighbourhood of 2–5 per cent of human bloods have this unpleasant capacity to harm those into which they are injected, but even so there is so much use made nowadays of blood and plasma transfusions as sheer life-saving measures that the numbers of cases of post-transfusion jaundice is not small. It seems that some people become infected with the serum hepatitis virus – how we do not know – and carry it in their blood for long periods without showing any symptoms. These are the dangerous donors of blood, and it is particularly unfortunate that so far there is no way whatever of sorting them out from people who are not carriers of the virus.

To return to the yellow fever vaccine, we have to explain how it happened to contain this virus derived from human blood. Yellow fever virus is a rather delicate organism, which is not easy to preserve in the living state that is essential if the vaccine is to be effective. After much experiment it was found that the virus could be preserved satisfactorily if it was frozen solid and then desiccated in the frozen state provided some suitable serum protein was included. It was thought that the most satisfactory serum protein to include, the one which would be least likely to raise any complications, was that from human blood. Unfortunately one large batch of human serum contained at least one contribution from a person with the dangerous virus-carrying blood, and all the vaccine which contained this batch of serum was able to produce jaundice in a considerable proportion of those inoculated. As soon as the nature of the jaundice was recognized the human serum was omitted from all subsequent batches of vaccine and no further trouble was encountered.

Perhaps there are two morals from this occurrence: the first that it is highly desirable that anything injected into human beings should be such that it can be definitely sterilized and proved to be sterile before use; the second that when the progress of medicine leads to some treatment or manipulation that has no analogies with anything natural – i.e. with anything encountered during the course of evolution – there are always liable to be unexpected and undesirable side actions. Blood transfusions, X-rays, and potent synthetic drugs, are all at times necessary life-savers, but the body has no wisdom in dealing with them and the physician must watch carefully lest he do more harm than good.

Dengue

Dengue fever is reported by those who have suffered it to be one of the most unpleasant diseases which involve no appreciable danger to life. It is typically a fever lasting five or six days with severe headaches and pains in the back and limbs, usually with a rash coming out towards the end of the fever. After recovering from the fever the patient may be left in a state of marked weakness and depression for some weeks.

Dengue can be responsible for some spectacular epidemics with victims numbered in hundreds of thousands. In 1928 for instance 90 per cent of the inhabitants of Athens were involved, and in a big epidemic in 1922 between one and two million people had dengue in Texas and other Southern states. In Australia dengue has shown an interesting periodicity of behaviour. It is constantly present but unobtrusive in the northern fringe of the continent. Epidemics have occurred at intervals of seven to ten years when the virus seems to move down the Queensland coast to Brisbane and the north of New South Wales, never quite reaching Sydney. The biggest was in 1925–6, when more than half a million people were involved, but the most important was probably in 1942. At one critical period more than half the American and Australian troops at Townsville and other Queensland centres were out of action from dengue.

Until very recently the virus was not found to be transmissible to any experimental animal and all the classical experiments were done with human volunteers. With a consistently non-fatal disease like dengue the problems of its study with human volunteers are mainly administrative, and most of the necessary facts were uncovered effectively and without fuss. There was strong circumstantial evidence that dengue was spread by *Aedes aegypti*, and this was proved experimentally in Australia in 1916. Important advances were made during the Second World War, when it was shown that the virus could be induced to cause infection in the brains of mice. Much of the work done at this time has only recently been described in print, and one catches a glimpse of a dilemma that is becoming familiar among microbiologists nowadays.

Dengue can be prevented wherever sanitary authorities are willing to see that measures to stop the breeding of *Aedes* larvae are enforced. This is undoubtedly the only practical way to prevent the disease, and from the community's point of view is all we need to know about dengue. When however a method is found by which a convenient laboratory animal becomes available for the study of the virus, wide new fields of investigation open up before any investigator of drive and imagination. There are undoubtedly just as subtle problems to be solved in regard to the natural history of dengue virus as with any other virus. Is there a jungle dengue analogous to the jungle yellow fever? Why does immunity to dengue appear to last for a much shorter time? Are there different immunological types of virus? Where does the virus multiply in the human body? and if, as seems likely, it also multiplies in the mosquito that carries it from man to man, in what cells of the insect does this multiplication occur? There are partial answers to some of these questions already, but the bigger question arises which bothers so many of us in the twentieth century. Where is all this detailed study of problems, which from the practical human point of view have been solved, leading us? Is it worth doing?

Two or three years ago I should have said unhesitatingly that the effective and competent study of any aspect of infectious disease was very much worth while both for its intrinsic interest and for the light that conclusions reached might throw on problems in related and perhaps more humanly important fields. Most medical scientists will still hold that point of view, and in a world where the arbitrary misuse of power was unthinkable, there could be no reason to counter it. To-day however I feel that there is an imperative need for biologists to look at the human and social implications of their science. Successes in medicine and particularly in the prevention of infectious disease have outstripped any appreciation of the overall ecological situation of the human species, and seem as likely to give rise to appalling new social problems in the long run as to save or prolong life in the short term. And, taking a narrower view, what is likely to be gained by the community from the detailed study of an infectious disease even by a brilliant investigator once the problem of its practical control has been solved? There may be an international reputation for the successful investigator, but one can wonder whether there will be any other use made of his facts than to help in forging some new weapon for the hands of those in a position to dominate their fellows.

I do not think that such thoughts had anything to do with the delay in publishing work that was done for the American Army on dengue fever, but I can sense there the beginnings of a doubt about the worth of what by all older criteria is 'first-rate work'.

CHAPTER FOURTEEN

THE EVOLUTIONARY ORIGIN OF VIRUSES, NEW DISEASES, AND THE POSSIBILITIES OF THE FUTURE

In all the preceding chapters I have as far as possible confined myself to the recording of established facts and of those deductions which spring directly from the facts. In this final chapter I should like to allow speculation a freer range – and to look at the past and the future of viruses in the light of what we know of their present status.

It is necessary first to be quite definite that the discussion will be wholly at the biological level – man being necessarily regarded as a mammalian species subject like every other animal to the struggle for existence against both parasites and predators. There is in fact no other legitimate approach to the problems of disease.

Virus disease of man then is regarded as the manifestation either of an almost stable equilibrium between the two species parasite and host – as exemplified by measles, influenza, or herpes – or of a temporary or accidental unstabilized association – as in yellow fever or poliomyelitis. The evolutionary problem concerns not the disease but the way in which the virus species originated and how it has survived.

There are, of course, no fossil bacteria or viruses, nor is there any known virus disease which could produce bony changes recognizable in fossils. Any discussion of probable lines of evolution must therefore be essentially speculation and deduction from the existing state of affairs. In the chapter on herpes the evidence was outlined for believing that two viruses, herpes of man and a virus of monkeys, must have persisted since the days when both hosts had a common ancestor, probably in the Oligocene period. Parasitism by micro-organism must have been a feature of life from the first appearance of multicellular plants and animals, and there is world enough and time for an infinity of mutation and adaptation amongst the parasites.

As the simplest and smallest form of life it might be tempting to think of viruses as surviving left-overs of some pre-cellular stage that arose in the very first phase of organic evolution. Most biologists have however discarded this possibility, largely because there is nothing about a virus that suggests a capacity to live at the expense of relatively simple chemical materials. There must have been precursors of the bacteria and unicellular algae, but once these forms appeared in something approaching their modern guise any less efficient sub-cellular forms would almost certainly have been utilized as food for bacteria and vanished. There are only two current hypotheses of viral evolution, both based on the necessity for viruses of strict intracellular growth. The most popular hypothesis, and the one I should support, is that viruses are derived by degenerate evolution from larger disease-producing micro-organisms such as bacteria or protozoa. The second is that all or some of the viruses producing animal disease are descendants of what were originally parts of the host cell. This second hypothesis is based on the fact that in every cell there are components which appear to be self-duplicating units producing more of themselves when required but always in conformity to the needs of the cell. The best known of such entities are the genes, the units which are responsible for determining the genetic characters of the organism. These are distributed in the chromosomes which form the most important part of the cell nucleus. Modern biological theory postulates in addition that there are self-duplicating units in the extra-nuclear part of the cell, the cytoplasm. If such a unit escaped from the normal controlling mechanisms and developed a capacity to multiply indefinitely at the expense of the other components in the cell, it would behave almost precisely as a virus. It is probably a fair statement of the position to say that those pathologists who are interested in the so-called 'cancer viruses' tend to favour such a theory or at least to regard it as a valid competitor with the hypothesis of parasitic degeneration. Those of us who are concerned with viruses which produce typical infectious disease are, I think, almost uniformly convinced that these viruses are independent organisms derived by degenerative evolutionary processes from larger micro-organisms.

It is, of course, impossible to *prove* such a hypothesis. The best pointer towards its truth is to be found in a comparison of the various types of micro-organism that cause disease from relatively large protozoa and bacteria down to the smallest virus. To make the series more complete we should also add the non-parasitic protozoa and bacteria from which the parasitic forms themselves probably evolved. To develop the full argument it would be necessary to assume a fairly detailed knowledge of bacteriology, and only a superficial covering will be attempted. It is generally accepted that primitive bacteria have a high capacity to synthesize all the components of their structure from simple chemical compounds. Mutations of such forms to types which will grow only if this or that substance which the parent form can synthesize is provided ready-made are readily observed in the laboratory. Most disease-producing bacteria resemble such mutants in their nutritional requirements. Living in body fluids or tissues which contain substances closely similar to those in bacterial substance, the bacterium does not need to have the same synthetic ability as one which lives wholly away from living tissues. There is a surprisingly close resemblance in the chemical structure of all forms of living substance, and in broad terms we may say that the more intimately a parasitic bacterium approaches the cell the less synthetic ability it requires. Where special abilities are not required for survival they tend with great regularity to be lost in the course of evolution. Where organisms grow within living cells it is common for them to have very complex nutritional requirements that cannot always be provided in the form of an artificial nutrient medium. The rickettsiae which have been mentioned in connexion with typhus fever look very like small bacteria, but they resemble viruses in being incapable of growth except in living cells. They may well be regarded as intermediates between highly parasitic bacteria, which live largely within cells but can be grown on special non-living media, and the larger viruses. Some of the larger viruses themselves, such as those responsible for psittacosis and the eye disease, trachoma, appear to be more closely related to the rickettsiae than to typical viruses such as those of small-pox or influenza. Like the rickettsiae their disease-producing action can be greatly reduced by the newer antibiotic drugs like aureomycin and chloromycetin.

As we move down the scale of size we obtain evidence of less and less complicated structure. The relatively large vaccinia virus shows no sign of the outer membrane, visible in electron microscope pictures of bacteria, rickettsiae, and psittacosis virus, but it has a complex chemical constitution which points to a considerable degree of organization, more than is found in the influenza virus. As we have seen in an earlier chapter, there is much indirect evidence that viruses increase in amount in the cell by a complex process that makes use of the cell's mechanisms. The virus provides as it were little more than patterns which force the cell to make more similar patterns and destroy itself in the process. A full discussion of this theory of parasitic degeneration would require much more consideration of the chemical processes of nutrition

and synthesis than would be appropriate here. It is possible
to say, however, that the theory finds many analogies amongst
the higher forms, worms, insects, and so on, that have taken on
a parasitic mode of life – and in the process lost many of the
faculties that their free-living ancestors possessed. In the light
of present knowledge it is much the most likely hypothesis
and is not incompatible with anything we know about viruses.

It is, of course, quite inadequate to think of viruses as
nothing more than degenerate bacteria or protozoa. They
must along with their overall degeneration have developed
specialized devices to favour the parasitic mode of life. The
mechanism we described earlier by which influenza viruses
make contact with the cell is probably one of these speciali-
zations. From the human point of view the long-term evolution of the viruses is of no particular importance. What are
important are the shorter term changes in virus character
by which new diseases appear or known diseases take on
new characters. Infectious disease is constantly changing its
pattern. Many of these changes are essentially of environmental origin, but almost all are associated with some change
in the character of the virus. In other chapters we have said
something about the appearance and extension of poliomyelitis epidemics in the last 70 years and about the disastrous
change in the character of influenza that took place in 1918.
In another place we told how smallpox infiltrated into England around 1600 and in the eighteenth century was the
dominant infectious disease of childhood, how it dwindled
in the nineteenth, and in the twentieth appeared in various
countries in a far milder guise. There are many other examples of changing disease patterns. For instance there are
detailed accounts of three epidemics, almost certainly virus
diseases, which in their time flourished, killed, and caused
great public alarm, then vanished in a few years and have not
reappeared. The first was the sweating sickness of the Tudor

period, the 'English sweats' of continental writers. The first epidemic seemed to come with Henry VII's French mercenaries from Bosworth Field in 1485. Soon after Henry and his troops arrived in London an acutely fatal epidemic broke out. High fever, redness of the face, and profuse sweating were the most conspicuous symptoms, and death might come within a day or two of the onset. It was noted that the disease seemed to attack particularly persons of wealth and distinction rather than poorer folk and adults rather than children. Three successive Lord Mayors of London died of the Sweats in a few months. The epidemic died down to be followed by four others at irregular intervals; the last and most severe in 1562 spread also over a large part of the Continent. Thereafter the disease vanished completely.

In 1916 a disease of unusual character was first described from Rumania. It was an infection of the brain giving rise to a variety of symptoms including an excessive sleepiness during the day and a tendency after recovery to develop the condition known as paralysis agitans in which the victim is constrained to slow tremulous movement of his limbs. It was called encephalitis lethargica. Over the next seven years it increased in frequency, first in Europe and then over all the rest of the world. The peak was reached in 1923 and thereafter cases began to occur less frequently and no certain cases have been reported since 1930. The disease never involved a large proportion of the population, but its results in those who survived were very distressing. No microorganism responsible for the disease was ever isolated, but all who studied it were convinced that a virus was involved.

The third example is a more local and less important one, the Australian X disease. In 1917–18 acute encephalitis (brain fever) began to be recognized over a wide area of 'outback' Australia. A semi-circular area with its centre at the town of Broken Hill, mainly involving New South Wales west of the Blue Mountains, but touching Queensland in the north and Victoria in the south, included almost all the cases. Cases were relatively rare, but many of them were fatal. Infection could be experimentally transmitted to monkeys, but methods of virus study were then in their infancy and no virus was preserved. It was thought in 1950 that the virus responsible might be one of those that had been isolated since 1930 in various parts of the world, but, as far as Australia was concerned, it appeared that after a small flare up at Broken Hill in 1925 the disease had vanished completely.

In the first edition of this book this was included as a disease that had come and gone and left no trace behind. Within a year of writing the paragraph a team from my own laboratory were hard at work investigating what was eventually proved to be a new outbreak of X disease, now known as Murray Valley encephalitis. The virus was isolated and compared with related viruses from other parts of the world; it was shown to be transmissible by mosquitoes and the riddle of its rare appearance in the inhabited parts of Australia was solved. Very briefly, the virus is normally a parasite of birds and mosquitoes in the tropics, and only when there is excessive and continued rainfall in early summer in Eastern Australia are the conditions right for the virus to move south into temperate regions. The story may point a moral or state a platitude, that a disease is mysterious only as long as the technical methods for its study are not available.

Similar episodes will doubtless be as characteristic of the future as of the past. With the improvements in technical methods of virus study one can be optimistic that new virus diseases will be effectively studied and in most cases a retrospective understanding of how they arose will be possible. It is much less likely that we shall ever be in a position to point to such and such a danger of new epidemic disease *before* it appears. What we have to realize is that infectious disease is only a visible manifestation of the complex and subtle processes by which micro-organisms survive. At any given moment any virus one likes to choose is in the form of a population of virus particles, some in various places outside of living cells, others actually multiplying in susceptible cells, sometimes with the production of disease, much more frequently without inducing any symptoms. Mutation within the multiplying population is constantly occurring and there is a strict winnowing for survival. When a virulent mutant finds a non-immune host population there is a sudden enormous increase in the size of the virus population, but equally likely are circumstances which will exterminate all but a minute proportion of the individuals making up the virus species. The measles virus reaches an isolated island community; within four or six weeks there is a raging epidemic and astronomical numbers of virus particles. In another month there may be no viable virus particles on the island. That particular branch of the species 'measles virus' has temporarily expanded like an explosion and then vanished as completely and permanently as its smoke.

One might guess that new 'virus' diseases most frequently arise by the emergence of a mutation in some virus that normally survives in hosts, either man or some animal, that are unaffected by its presence. An interesting example first came under laboratory notice in 1948. By using the method of inoculating baby mice born not more than five days previously it is possible to isolate very frequently from intestinal contents or sewage one or other of a group of viruses not very distantly related to polio virus. These are the Coxsackie viruses, named after the little town in up-state New York where they were first isolated. In the great majority of cases the presence of one of these virus in the intestine produces no symptoms whatever. It is probable that moderately often they produce mild symptoms of fever and other signs which may mimic the early stage of an attack of polio, but they never give rise to paralysis.

At rather long intervals there appear epidemics of a mild disease in which the main symptom is acute muscular pain often felt in the side or upper abdomen. It is not at all uncommon for the mistaken diagnosis of appendicitis to be made if the doctor does not know that an epidemic of this sort is in progress. The disease is known as Bornholm disease – the first description came from that island in the Baltic – epidemic myalgia or pleurodynia. It is now clear that Bornholm disease is the result of infection by one or other of several immunological types of Coxsackie virus. In addition, it has been shown that two other types of relatively minor diseases are due to viruses of this group – a sore throat with small blisters on the tonsil and palate called herpangina and a benign form of meningitis which in 1953 was very prevalent in Sydney, Australia. At least 17 immunological types of Coxsackie viruses have been isolated from human faeces in various parts of the world and there is nothing to suggest that the list is yet complete. Here then in our own bowels we have a potential reservoir of new virus diseases. Suppose the potential power of the Coxsackie viruses to attack muscles was greatly enhanced in a certain mutant and circumstances allowed it to spread freely. I can imagine as a result a completely new type of epidemic in which intense generalized pain in the muscles would immobilize the victims, many of whom would die with symptoms of acute heart failure when the muscles of the heart were involved. There has never been an epidemic of this sort, but equally there has never since 1560 been an epidemic with the symptoms of the English Sweats.

There are possibilities, too, that benign infections of birds or animals may find new opportunities of transfer to man, particularly if appropriate mutants arise around the same time. In 1933 an epidemic arose in St Louis of what was then a wholly new type of encephalitis. It is now known that the St Louis virus is an almost harmless parasite of birds spread from one to the other in the nest by mites and carried over longer distances and to different hosts by mosquitoes. It is still not clear whether the human epidemic resulted from some change in the environmental circumstances or arose essentially because of a mutation in the virus.

I have heard public health administrators criticize modern virus research, saying that all the important infectious diseases are now under control and that it is of dubious value to study, at great expense, the relatively trivial diseases, influenza, the common cold, Coxsackie virus infections, Q fever, on which so many virologists are working. Superficially the criticism is logical enough, but there is a more than adequate answer. We cannot afford to neglect the scientific study of any phase of the universe that impinges even ever so slightly on human welfare, for the simple reason that we can never be certain that that contact may not suddenly become all important.

Every virus that has been studied has shown itself capable of giving rise to mutants of lower and higher virulence. It is probably correct to regard viruses as the most labile and mutable of all living organisms. I suspect that for a new variant to arise and initiate an epidemic of a 'new' disease, a very rare combination of mutations plus specially favourable environmental circumstances will be required. But remember that viruses during an epidemic will number their component individuals in figures like 10^{16}, that their generation-time is at most a few hours, and it is easy to see that even extraordinarily rare combinations of circumstances can be expected to occur. In a sense every virus that can multiply in mammalian cells is a potential threat to human life and justifies full investigation.

And at this point we reach the characteristic dilemma of this twentieth century. Every aspect of virus disease justifies full investigation. From such investigation we may hope for improved means of preventing or curing disease, but equally

the fuller our knowledge becomes the greater the threat of
the use of that same knowledge for the deliberate dissemina-
tion of disease in war or in some other phase of the incessant
struggle for power amongst men. We cannot refuse to face
the position that we have just entered an era of extraordinarily
effective biological research, an era that may be as productive
as the golden age of atomic research that reached a provisional
culmination in Hiroshima and Nagasaki. Laboratory research
is at least as potent to produce new evils as to counter existent
ones. Until World War II it was accepted that biological research and medical research were almost synonymous – that
the objective in studying bacteriology was to prevent and cure
infectious disease, that the justification for animal experiments
in physiology was similarly to be found in its contribution to
the practice of curative medicine. Things have been gradually
changing since 1939. The greatest practical application of
enzyme chemistry has been not in the treatment of disease
but in the synthesis of one group of specific enzyme poisons –
anti-cholinesterases to the bio-chemist, 'nerve gases' to the
man in the street. These are war gases of a wholly different
order of danger from the chlorine and mustard gas of the first
World War. With every new advance in the understanding of
the chemistry of vital enzyme actions there automatically arise
new possibilities for the production of tailor-made custom-
built specific poisons for those enzymes – new war gases in
short. In the field of infectious disease most thought about
bacterial warfare in the past has been at a rather elementary
level – to poison wells with dysentery, to liberate rats infected
with plague bacilli or to spray a city from the air with anthrax
bacilli. Up to the present we have had to accept agents of
disease as we found them in so far as their capacity to spread
or to kill was concerned. In the laboratory it was almost the
invariable rule that both these capacities rapidly diminished
as bacteria were cultivated. To a lesser extent this was (and is)

also the case with viruses transferred to laboratory hosts. But things are changing rapidly. We are beginning to learn what are the conditions under which a bacterium retains its maximal virulence, how sometimes a bacterium can become resistant to a drug without losing its virulence, and with each such advance the potentialities of bacteriological warfare increase.

I doubt if any war department has yet thought seriously about the use of viruses in war. Yet in the insane logic of power politics the ultimate weapon is the virus disease which will spread through and destroy those unwilling to accept domination but spare those who have submitted. I see no reason why with the continuation of current types of research it should not be physically possible to produce such a weapon in twenty or thirty years' time. In preceding chapters enough has been said to show in very general outline how the new viruses that have arisen spontaneously in the past might in the future be produced by deliberate action, and how once produced it might be possible to immunize against them. The initiation of the spread of a new hyper-virulent virus disease as an act of war is not a threat of the immediate future, yet I think that it is as implicit in the lines of present-day virus research as atomic bombs were when U238 was shown in 1939 to undergo fission when bombarded with neutrons.

I suppose that it is as futile for a biologist to underline the potentialities of his science for war as for an atomic physicist, yet I think that all of us must continue to do so. War in the hands of modern science is an intolerable solution of the problem of power.

There is no branch of human activity that has been more successful in attaining its desired object than medical bacteriology with its practical application to the prevention of disease. It has succeeded essentially because within its field there have been few external obstructions or internal inhibitions against an objective consideration of man as a mammal subject to the same attack by micro-organisms as any other mammal. The experimental method applied directly to animal infections has provided answers that in most cases have been triumphantly successful when transferred to the corresponding human problems.

Is it altogether too naïve to wonder if the same attitude could not be applied to the problems of human conflict that have plagued history? What is to prevent our taking the same mental approach towards such problems as is accepted as normal in dealing with infectious disease? To a biologist there are problems at two levels. The ecological situation can perhaps best be expressed by asking what are the requirements that will allow the human species to survive indefinitely without exhausting the irreplaceable resources of the planet and without falling significantly below its present average level of mental and physical health. The second group of problems concern the intrinsic springs of human conflict that are expressed in the desire for power, in the importance attached to status, to prestige, to 'face', in aggressiveness and conversely in loyalty and subservience. Just as the ecological situation can be broadly equated with the problem of survival that confronts every living species from virus to mammal, so similar conflict situations can be observed and studied within every gregarious or semi-gregarious species of mammal or bird. There is a growing literature on group behaviour and dominance relations in animals, and anyone reading it cannot fail to be impressed with the extraordinary resemblance to human behaviour, especially in regard to situations of the types that lead to conflict.

Some day biologists and sociologists will agree that they have a common approach from the study of animal behaviour to the sources of human conflict. It seems to me that neither the exposition of the relevant facts of mammalian behaviour nor the transition to the objective aspects of typical human tensions and conflicts would be beyond the average man's capacity to understand. If in an appropriately simplified and acceptable form such an approach could filter down through the community there might develop an attitude towards war analogous to that which now exists towards infectious disease.

It is not so long since the germ theory of disease was either unintelligible or unacceptable to the best minds in Europe. To-day every housewife has an elementary knowledge of the process of infection and of simple methods of sterilization and on the whole applies that knowledge effectively. Throughout the community, too, there is a readiness to accept such mildly unpleasant practical measures as quarantine and immunization without resentment. If a scientific approach to problems of power and conflict equally soundly based could be built up, if it could be simplified, interpreted and disseminated in basically similar fashion to become something that all men could understand; then I think we might see develop a similar readiness to accept measures needed to prevent wars or to solve established conflicts.

We have seen the emergence of the atomic bomb, we know of the threat of the nerve gases, and if the present lines of research continue we can be certain that sooner or later lethal and controllable bacteriological weapons will be available. The simple application of the scientific method by men of high but not unusual intelligence will ensure that in all these fields the new weapons will steadily increase in effectiveness. The tools by which any group of men possessing power can extend and maintain their domination are becoming so powerful that one can almost speak of the appearance of a sharp discontinuity in the historical process. The only conceivable solution is to understand and by understanding seek to control those biological urges which become evident in the way men view themselves in relation to other men. If democracy can survive long enough it might be possible to provide insight into the processes concerned – for the rulers as well as for the ruled.

Famine, pestilence, and war are the three great evils from which men have always prayed to be delivered. Within a hundred years the second of these evils has been removed almost in its entirety by the work of a few thousand men guided by the ideas of six men of genius: Koch, Pasteur, Ehrlich, Theobald Smith, Dubos, Goodpasture. Only a medical bacteriologist who has seen with understanding the last twenty-five years of that greatest of social revolutions could be expected to dream that one day war might similarly be dealt with. Human behaviour is as much a subject for scientific study as influenza or yellow fever, and sooner or later an adequate understanding of the processes by which one man dominates another will emerge. That understanding represents the only substantial hope of curbing the malignant concentration of power that seems to lie ahead of us. I believe that there is no other approach to effective knowledge than the scientific method, and I believe that only knowledge can counter evil that makes use of knowledge.

INDEX

BIOLOGY AND PHYSIOLOGY

Animals Without Backbones – Ralph Buchsbaum

An account of the invertebrates, containing in all 128 pages of illustrations (A187, A188). 2 volumes   each 3s 6d

Beyond the Microscope – Kenneth M. Smith

An account of the viruses that are responsible for many human, animal, and plant diseases, and how they are combated (A119)   2s

Human Physiology – Kenneth Walker

The human body, how it works, and the relation of body and mind to disease (A102)   2s

Man and the Vertebrates – A. S. Romer

The counterpart of *Animals Without Backbones*, in two volumes, both illustrated (A303, A304). 2 volumes each 3s 6d

The Personality of Animals – H. Munro Fox

How much animals' lives depend on their senses, 'instinct', 'intelligence', and a capacity to learn, with accounts of recent experiments (A78)   2s

The Physical Basis of Personality – V. H. Mottram

A discussion of the laws of heredity and of the interplay between physical and mental factors in personality (A139) 2s

PSYCHOLOGY

Child Care and the Growth of Love – John Bowlby

A summary of the author's 1951 report on the importance of mother-love in the development of a child's character and personality, and the problem of the motherless child (A271)
2s 6d

A Dictionary of Psychology – James Drever

Definitions and explanations of the terms used in psychology, psychiatry, and the mental sciences. A volume in the series of Penguin Reference Books (R5)
2s 6d

The Intelligent Parents' Manual – F. Powdermaker and L. Grimes

A well-known discussion of the problems of parenthood from the child's birth through infancy to adolescence, in a new edition revised by Cyril Bibby (PH20)
2s 6d

The Psychology of Sex – Oswald Schwarz

How to deal with the problems raised by the sexual instinct in the lives of juvenile and adult, analysing the interaction of the physical urge and the moral principle (A194)
2s 6d

The Personality of Man – G. N. M. Tyrrell

An account of modern achievements and techniques in the field of psychical research (A165)
2s 6d

NEW PELICANS

A Short History of Confucian Philosophy – Liu Wu-Chi

A book for the general reader who wants to know at first hand about China's greatest philosophy, which has moulded the Chinese nation for almost twenty-five centuries. (A 333)
2s 6d

Man on his Nature – Sir Charles Sherrington

An invigorating expression of a biologist's philosophy, described by the *Sunday Times* as 'one of the landmarks in the history of man's speculation'. (A 322)†
2s 6d

Man, Morals and Society – J. C. Flugel

'Those who wish to know what psycho-analysis has to say on fundamental moral problems will here find an exposition written with great clarity and candour, based on a thorough grasp of all the relevant data and likely to stimulate further inquiry'. *The Spectator*. (A 324)*
3s 6d

The Colour Problem – A. H. Richmond

A study of colour prejudice, racial discrimination, and social separation, with an account of racial relations and the 'colour-bar' in British and Commonwealth territories in Africa and the West Indies. (A 328)
3s 6d

Sex and Society – Kenneth Walker and Peter Fletcher

The psychological and social implications of various topics related to sex are here discussed in the belief that human sexuality is more than an autonomous function and involves the whole personality. (A 332)
2s 6d

* Not for sale in the U.S.A.
† Not for sale in the U.S.A. or Canada

NEW PELICANS

Animal Painting in England – Basil Taylor

This survey from Barlow to Landseer has seventy plates, of which six are in colour, an introductory essay, biographies of the artists, notes on the plates, and a bibliography. (A 251)
3s 6d

Bird Recognition 3 – James Fisher

The third volume in this series, describing the appearance, life, and habits of the rails, game-birds, and larger perching and singing birds, with many maps and charts and nearly seventy illustrations by 'Fish-Hawk'. (A 177)
3s 6d

Electricity – Eric de Ville

Its discovery, the landmarks of its history, its use and modern developments are clearly explained with the aid of 16 pages of plates and many line drawings in the text. (A 323)
2s 6d

Microbes and Us – Hugh Nicol

This book draws attention to the fact that man must either go on offering oblations of fossil fuel to the inhabitants of the soil, or suffer the consequences. (A 326)
2s 6d

Porcelain through the Ages – George Savage

A survey of the main porcelain factories of Europe and Asia with 64 pages of plates, many line drawings, a bibliography, and tables of makers' marks. (A 298)
5s